When Albert Einstein was asked if he believed in God,
his answer was simple:

*"There's got to be something
behind all that energy."*

WHY WE AND THE UNIVERSE EXIST

EINSTEIN'S

BY ROY MASTERS

Edited by Robert Just

FINDING GOD
IN PHYSICS

MISSING RELATIVE

FINDING GOD IN PHYSICS:
EINSTEIN'S MISSING RELATIVE

Published by the Foundation of Human Understanding

Printed in the United States of America

For information, contact:
The Foundation of Human Understanding
P.O. Box 1009
Grants Pass, Oregon 97528
Call: 1-800-877-3227

The Foundation of Human Understanding
Website address: http://www.fhu.com

Library of Congress Catalogue Card Number: 97-77602

ISBN 0-933900-19-8

Cover Photo: Star-Birth Clouds • M16 Hubble Space Telescope • WPFC2PRC95-
44b • November 2, 1995 • J.Hester and P. Scowen (AZ Univ.) NASA/Space
Telescope Science Institute/Association of Universities for Research in
Astronomy, Inc.

Book design by David Masters

ACKNOWLEDGMENTS

It would not have been possible to finish this work without the insight, the exquisite editing skill, and the patience of my friend Robert Just. My thanks also go to three other friends for their good work: Dorothy Baker, my faithful editor of over thirty years, as well as colleagues David Kupelian and Wen Smith.

Roy Masters

TABLE OF CONTENTS

PREFACE
THE END OF CHAOS

*"The whole of science is nothing more
than a refinement of everyday thinking."*

Albert Einstein, *Physics and Reality*, 1936

Around the time the Hubble telescope was sending the world all those thrilling early pictures, opening up grand new vistas for cosmology, I got a phone call from Roy Masters. I was helping him edit this his first science book and Roy was excited to show me something he had discovered that related to his cosmic origin theory. I live only 10 minutes away so I hopped in my car wondering what it could be. He had mentioned his pool pump but I couldn't imagine what connection he had drawn between cosmology and a swimming pool. Whatever the idea, I knew it was going to be fun to talk about.

When I arrived Roy was sitting on the base of the diving board looking down at the deep sunlit water. The high pressure pump shot an even flow of fresh water into the pool which caused swirls beneath the surface. But that wasn't what intrigued Roy. He was focused on shadows cast on the bottom of the pool. They exploded into existence seemingly out of nowhere, a fractured symmetry of shadows, some so black you would think they were caused by a solid object floating on the surface. Roy eagerly pointed out that these myriad shadows were the result of the swirls made by the water flowing evenly into the pool. Some swirls were loose and left fleeting gray shadows; other swirls were tight spinning and left those dark, "solid" shadows.

The effect was a spectacular mimicry of Masters' theory of original matter—a big whoosh, or as he calls it, a "God Bang" of pre-time force swirling into this dimension—a "pre-physical" force causing original motion, building pressure, and then clumping into whirlpools whose very spin creates weight/resistance in gyroscopic fashion. The result of this sudden creation is an apparently random explosion of primal matter (what Masters has named "origitrons"). That afternoon we watched a similar display occurring on the bottom of the pool. I can only imagine what we looked like to Roy's grandchildren as we sat by the pool staring down at the water, but for me, it was a fascinating, poetic moment—and typical of how this man theorizes, full of child-like wonder and irrepressible curiosity despite his nearly 70 years of age.

The pool analogy didn't have to be perfect. For Roy, the point was simple and beautiful: Out of something invisible, motion alone can create something real enough to cast a shadow. We were both transfixed, watching shadows on the bottom of the pool suddenly form, sometimes join, live, and die in an organic display of force made tangible—something apparently coming from nothing. Of course, "apparently" is the operative word.

Like a child pulling apart and puzzling over a clock just to see how it works, Roy Masters maintains his delight at each stage of the journey he takes within the pages of this book. He uses repetition not solely to clarify and persuade, although certainly that first, but also because he so enjoys every step of his adventure that he can't help but repeat the key theories discovered along the way. Call it an experiment in pure thinking. The point is not to be right at every turn, but to be bold in following the path, following simple principles, no matter where they lead, even if that means daring to rethink gravity or to question current beliefs about light.

Let younger thinkers challenge the theories presented herein. Let them add or subtract from them, or even dismiss them out of hand, but in the process let them ponder the unfathomable mysteries of the cosmos—ponder the behavior of light as it slows down to pass through a prism and then, inexplicably—in fact, impossibly—regains its original speed. This kind of mystery spawns the pure excitement of science, the desire to discover and to know more intimately.

Whatever reaction the reader has to this little book, Masters' theories are an effort to answer some of science's unanswered questions and to provide a basis for empirical discovery. Roy's passionate pursuit of a unified field theory is admittedly an intuitive journey based on his belief that the physical laws of the cosmos are logical, and ultimately point to the doorway through which the cosmos came, not as a chaotic Big Bang, but as an orderly flow—a God Bang.

THE WONDER OF A LIVING UNIVERSE

*"Science without religion is lame,
religion without science is blind."*

Albert Einstein

Gazing at one of the Hubble telescope's most stunning photographs, showing pre-born stars gestating as particle clouds 7 trillion light years long, I remembered how marvelous even the simple night sky seemed to me when I was a boy. As most children do, I used to gaze at the stars in wonder. I especially marveled at one particular idea, that the universe was infinite. No ending?—not possible! And yet if it did end, or simply curve into itself, what lay beyond it? A forever void, or maybe even another dimension? Whatever it was, I knew there would have to be something—and how long did that "something" extend out into the darkness? No matter how "far" I could think, I knew I could measure nothing of infinity.

Each thought only increased my awe at the mystery. As I looked into the night sky, the jewel-like stars piercing the black would fade from my consciousness. Focused only on the blackness, I tried but couldn't succeed in imagining a universe that literally—literally!—did not come to an end. While I contemplated the infinite cosmos, spiritual wonderment and scientific wonderment became almost the same thing. This book is about such wonderment. It seeks the realm where physics meets metaphysics, where the unknowable is perceived through the knowable, where science joins religion as an intuitive, inward calling, and not merely an outward discipline to be learned.

Bringing the Divine into the scientific realm would seem an impossible goal. So much of religious thinking requires a leap of faith, while science is more immediately graspable. Yet if God is alive and if this is His universe, then at some point God created the discernible principles we call science. That moment was the beginning of science, a systematic connection between metaphysics and physics. Creation occurs where the unknowable and the knowable meet and commingle. Predictably, the closer science comes to the metaphysical border, the more unfamiliar science will seem. This book approaches that border.

Even for religious people this "God Science" may seem strange. After all, science in this century has always been something foreign to faith. The widely accepted interpretation of a chaotic Big Bang tends to leave us feeling that we are at the "far end" of creation, physically (although not spiritually) separated from the Creator. We are left believing that God's miracles have little or no relationship to science; we think of miracles as leaps over science. However, if God created reality, why is it hard to believe that He connects directly to the very scientific laws He created—that He even makes miracles by way of those laws? In an age of genetic and molecular manipulation, is "water into wine" so hard to fathom? After all, we know matter is nothing more than organized energy.

The pure fascination of the book you are about to read lies where the metaphysical and the physical meet, where one dimension actually comes into, creates, and connects to another. Hard to imagine? Try contemplating infinity and you'll get a good idea of what you are headed for.

GOD BANG:
THE BEGINNING OF SCIENCE

"The most incomprehensible
thing about the universe
is that it is comprehensible."

Albert Einstein

Masters asks us to imagine that the universe is not what we think it is, not scattered and unfathomable, but formed in an organized and sensible way—as simple and as beautiful as Einstein envisioned. Imagine a new paradigm of physics, one so powerful that it startles us all out of our normal patterns of thinking—a revolution in 21st Century science. Is such a thing possible in our lifetime? We usually think such revolutions happen only to other generations and yet, thanks to the Hubble telescope, the field of cosmology waits like an expectant mother; great new discoveries are on the way, and everyone knows it. Now, in this environment full of eager anticipation, the author invites you to consider the following questions:

What if space is not void, but full of a force, similar to the space *aether* proposed by many scientists up through the 19th Century?

What if this force is both the original energy that created the universe, and the energy that acts upon it today as gravity (not the pulling force we have learned about but, instead, a *pushing* force)? What if this "pre-time force" (which we perceive as time) manifests everywhere in the cosmos not only as gravity force, but conceivably, as all other forces—an interconnected mother field—perhaps the "unified field" physicists have sought for so many years?

The impact of such a newly discovered reality would have a tremendous effect on the way we look at our place in the universe. Why? Well, imagine a force that energizes the whole universe while at the same time energizing the atoms in our bodies. A force like that would be both universal and completely personal. Imagine how it would change the way we think about physics, no longer as a mechanical system, distant and cold, but rather as something fluid, almost living, and functioning in close relationship to us.

Thus Masters proposes an origin event that was not a chaotic explosion, scattering matter across the cosmos, but rather an intimate, systematic expression of God's Will by way of a creation force pushed into this dimension. Masters claims that the resulting cosmos is a direct, continuing expression of that original force, first revealed more as a cold bang (that became heated under its own pressure) than the hot core explosion popularly theorized. The explosive effect of both "bangs" would be the same, as primal matter is flung out, evolving into larger energy/mass forms. Yet, that is where the basic similarity ends.

In the Masters paradigm, the whole cosmos is an organic creation flowing from a single initial force that is possibly still creating matter today. In its cold bang origin, this force acted more like a "light switch" than a "lightning bolt." That is, its sudden force not only exploded, but then flowed continually, and so has today a quality of perpetual origin-connection—a "God Bang" rather than a Big Bang. Yes, it behaves as an explosion does, but just as a light bulb explodes in a flash—and stays on—this whole universe is run by a continuous flow of energy that once lit, stays lit. The day may come, says Masters, when we shall harness this force (time and gravity to us), and use it to sail to the stars.

The preceding provides only a glimpse of the myriad theories and insights presented in the little book you have in your hand. The author's hope is to inspire the reader with the possibility of it all, not as an end, but as a beginning. Roy Masters believes that the truly incredible discoveries of God's science are yet to come. The 19th Century ended with statements that God is dead. In the following pages you will find the assertion that God is very much alive, and is keeping you alive—energizing your inner cosmos, your atoms and molecules, and maintaining their whirling energies. Meanwhile, His cosmos, His outer space, is also alive, held up, nourished, and directed by way of this same perpetual pre-time/time force that is the unified field Einstein so earnestly sought all his life. According to Masters, Einstein was on the right track; he was simply missing the Ultimate Relative.

Robert Just
November 27, 1997

How to Read this Book

*"I want to know how God created this world. I
am not interested in this or that phenomenon,
in the spectrum of this or that element. I want
to know God's thoughts, the rest are details."*

Albert Einstein

This book is only intended to point in a direction, not to present a complete and flawless theory to which one may not contribute. If the theory is sound, there are formulas to write and empirical studies to be undertaken.

In any case, as an amateur scientist I have enjoyed this journey filled with years of wondering and looking deeply into the things of nature, especially the mysteries of physics and cosmology. I can only hope that those who read this book will find in it some of the joy I found in writing it.

If only one part of this theory touches you deeply, then let that be your guide. Science is just beginning, especially for the young. There is much ahead that is exciting. It is my hope that, young or old, you will find clues in the following pages that will inspire you to seek a higher truth, a more accurate vision than is presented in these pages—and perhaps to find for yourself the only inspiration in life that really matters, the one that will help you face the final moments of your life with dignity, grace, and hope.

Roy Masters

INTRODUCTION

"It is certain, and evident to our senses, that in the world some things are in motion. Now whatever is moved is moved by another, for nothing can be in motion except it is in potentiality to that towards which it is moved; whereas a thing moves inasmuch as it is in act...It is therefore impossible that in the same respect and in the same way a thing could be both mover and moved, i.e., that it could move itself. Therefore, whatever is moved must be moved by another...But this cannot go on to infinity, because then there would be no first mover, and consequently, no other mover... Therefore, it is necessary to arrive at the first mover, moved by no other; and this everyone understands to be God."

St. Thomas Aquinas

When theologian Thomas Aquinas was on his deathbed, his assistant pleaded with him to finish his last book. Aquinas said, "I cannot." Urged once again, Aquinas said, "All that I have written is like chaff to me." And then he explained the mystical value of knowledge in his search for God:

That which is not known cannot be loved. Knowledge, therefore, is not to be loved for itself but is meant to lead to that which must be loved. When He whom is to be loved is found by virtue of knowledge, knowledge ceases.

****

Because people used to believe that the earth was flat, mariners were afraid to sail beyond the horizon for fear of falling off the edge of the world. The "authorities" of that age were also convinced the earth was flat; they rejected theories that stated otherwise, and they were certainly not interested in proof they were wrong.

Twentieth Century scientists who assume a Godless universe are like those "authorities" of old who believed in a flat earth. The more the evidence points to a universal design, and therefore a Designer, the more these kinds of scientists become petrified and frozen in their 20th Century belief system. Although modern physicists have studied the mysteries of the photon, electron, and quark, they are now stuck at the border of the greater mystery—the source of all this energy. Many are simply afraid to see there is more to science than knowledge of the facts—afraid to delve honestly into the metaphysics of physics. If God exists, then He must have created science and thus, honest scientific inquiry will lead directly back to Him.

The 20th Century has revealed many remarkable discoveries, from Einstein's Theory of Relativity to Quantum Physics, all edging us closer to understanding the origin of the universe. Generations of modern physicists probed deeper into the mysteries of nature's building blocks, and each time these physicists thought they fully understood their discovery. But then startling revelations led the next generation still deeper into the mysteries of atomic and subatomic particles.

There is small, smaller, and smallest, and then...nothing—or so these physicists say—just a passive void in the vast micro-interior which is part of the vast macro-exterior void of space. But how can super-energized subatomic complexities be the spawn of a passive nothing? Many physicists attribute universal force to a big explosion of some kind, but whatever the original energizing force is, two things must be true about it. First, something caused it, and that something has to be prephysical (or metaphysical). And second, that prephysical cause must be the basis of all the physical laws of the universe. In other words, it must be the Ultimate Relative—all creation being the expression of the Creator.

The next generation of physicists must take a final scientific step, and face the only thing left that truly exists beyond the theoretical void—the reality of God Himself. His living universe is not void space, but rather a force of primordial energy continually flowing throughout the universe.

Like the authorities of Columbus's day, most modern scientists do not listen enough to that "still small voice within," the same "voice" that urged Columbus on that "unseeable way" he followed despite his own fears. Columbus had vision, a knowing faith compelling him to go beyond. He knew without knowing why he knew, and he acted, not completely understanding the hand that pressed him forward.

This quality of vision-faith will be needed to create the new physics of the next century, needed to take that step into the unknown so that it might be known. However, in this final voyage we have no vessel, as Columbus did, to transport us, no compass to guide us, no tangible destination to verify our theory. How then shall we proceed? Shall we cringe on shore, staring at the horizon, stopped at the threshold of this ultimate adventure just because we cannot see or prove what lies out there? Or shall we venture forth unafraid, sailing a theoretical vessel into the unknown of new physics?

Unlike the physics of the great philosopher scientists, like Albert Einstein and others before him, modern physics tends to limit itself to mathematical calculations as the pathway to discovery. Yet, what physicists study as creation is only the physical phenomenon, rather than its noumenon (or cause of the phenomenon). The noumenon of a God-created universe is unfathomable to a secular scientist. Just as a mountain climber can reach the top of a mountain but, having no wings, can go no further, so also are many physicists ill-equipped to scale the reality of the originating other dimension. Their typically mathematical approach to the time/space/matter relationship cannot penetrate the noumenon of the "before now"— the other dimensional reality before time.

The purely mathematical mind cannot cross this border; neither can those who practice the more empirical methods of discovery. Instruments of science are made of subatomic particles; they can only measure what they know, in other words, what they are themselves. The "beyond" is beyond them.

Once we stand at the border of the "beyond," staring out over the very edge of creation, we need more than empirical study and ordinary theory; we need the very highest and purest form of scientific enlightenment. Speaking to us through that "still small voice," God guides our intuitive mind across the dimensional border to a deep comprehension of His magnificent creation and its ultimate principles. In the final analysis, mathematical formulas and scientific instruments cannot go where the soul can venture.

Currently, physics stands just about as close to the edge as it can get, having followed the cosmological trail of relative effects and causes. We have traced our physical reality almost all the way back to its Source. Yet, we shrink from this Source, looking for more superficial causes and effects—more knowledge. We avoid the philosophically obvious—that there must be an ultimate Uncaused Cause, a permanent root simplicity that relates to the physical universe just as the mathematical "zero" gives reality to the "one," and together they cause the whole complexity of mathematics to be born.

At the beginning of the 20th Century, Einstein began his journey of relatives, but he did not finish his voyage into the unknown dimension. Now as our knowledge increases, as we chart the 21st Century, physics needs to take on a "religious" quest because at the core of Einstein's profound theories there is a Missing Relative. The aim of this book is to seek out this Missing Relative that unifies physics, to seek out this Simplicity that explains the science it created.

One

BIG BANG'S LITTLE PROBLEM

"For the scientist who has lived by faith in the power of his reason, the story ends like a bad dream. He has scaled the mountains of ignorance; he is about to conquer the highest peak; as he pulls himself over the final rock, he is greeted by a small band of theologians, who have been sitting there for centuries."

Astrophysicist Robert Jastrow

The fact that the universe appears to be expanding leads cosmologists to conclude the universe was created by a hot, explosive event they call the "Big Bang." However, there are some questions with regard to this theory, beginning with the little problem of the "singularity," that infinitely dense, infinitely hot mass which science says caused the explosion. How did it get there in the first place, and where did all the heat come from? And then there's the big problem of time; when did it exist, and how? In the process of considering these and other limitations of a hot bang theory, another possibility of creation comes to mind—a cold bang that requires no pre-bang mass or time, but simply requires God.

Science says, rightly in my view, that the universe is expanding. But even with our light-sensitive technology, how do we really know? If we are indeed peering across billions of light years of space as they say, looking backwards into time at light reaching our telescopes from an expanding universe, then is it not possible that the expansion we see coming from the past is no longer happening back there right now? What is happening out there in the distant galaxies will surely not be seen for another few billion years. So how can we be so sure of an ever-expanding universe, merely by observation? What we see now is really ancient history. For all we know, the universe could already be collapsing. I am only trying to make the point that there are some things in science that cannot be fathomed by calculation based on observation. Observation as scientific technique cannot go far enough. It needs the partner of Einsteinian intuitive observation (looking through the mind's eye) based on sound philosophical theory establishing principles which then can be confirmed through scientific observation.

Pure scientific observation is not enough to complete the cosmological quest. Telescopes which can only register starlight reaching us now from billions of years ago cannot possibly know what is happening to those stars where they are now. It is not that telescopes are wrong in what they observe; they are just physically too time bound. Of course, empirical research in cosmology is always physically time bound and thus always limited.

The startling reality of Einstein's achievements is that he leaped ahead of empirical science through his unique intuitive approach. His inspired deductive powers gave mankind an understanding far ahead of mere mortal observation. The reason Einsteinian science is so important as a partner to observation is that there is a natural limit to human observation, a barrier beyond which we cannot go. Because we are time bound, there is a limit to what we can see, and thus, Einsteinian *second sight,* not being time bound, can penetrate the natural barrier of space/time and fathom the mysteries that elude our telescopes.

At the risk of belaboring the point, let me put this another way. What if there were an astronomer on some far flung planet in space, billions of light years away, looking at us with our light that has traveled all that distance in time to him? Could he not conclude that our movement is away from him, due to light's red shift? Could he not be under the same impression as we are in perceiving a young universe in its early stages? So which way is the past? And which way is out? It's all relative to who does the looking.

There is no way of knowing by observation what is happening out there now. As far as past and future are concerned, it is not possible to know about a "beginning" from our frame of reference. We simply don't know where it is or which way it is. It matters not that we on Earth are moving out with this so-called universal expansion. The fact remains that we are looking out at billions of years of ancient cosmological events, and they (if alien astronomers exist), looking back at us, would see us as nearer to the beginning of the creation event.

Now, the universe may well be expanding, but as I said, some things cannot ever be known by calculation from observation, simply because a calculation based upon such things as "which way is past" is flawed.

QUESTIONING THE BIG BANG THEORY

Let us look at the basic problem of an atheistic Big Bang Creation Theory which begins with "something" infinitely dense and infinitely hot—whatever that means—with no explanation about what it really is, whence it came, or how it actually came into being.

It is claimed that the entire universe sprang from what physicists call a singularity, perhaps "something" only as large as the period at the end of this sentence. Whatever the size, the very concept of an already existing "something" (large or small) is a contradiction in terms of science. In a real beginning, none of the laws of science would have existed. There was no such thing as size, dimension, mass, time, length, depth, width, heat, not to mention the dynamics of what they call a "bang."

A mass of infinite density, infinite temperature, infinitely small and compressed, is an *already existing* creation. So we must ask ourselves this question: What is this "thing"—infinitely small, dense, and hot—that already existed before the "Big Bang"? From where did it come, and how did it exist without time and space in which to exist? Nothing can exist in this dimension without space/time to precede its existence.

ORDER TO CHAOS TO ORDER?

A clump of infinite density cannot possibly explain creation. Who or what made this lump so compressed that when it was unleashed or unlocked, it exploded into the infinite expanse of the universe? What is the mechanism that triggered the bang? Again, we are alluding to laws of science that didn't yet exist. And what is the underlying law of a chaotic explosion like the Bang? Can lightning strike a junkyard and create a brand new Mercedes? Where is the meaningful unfolding order, the scientific progression of causes and effects?

A big bang is an explosive/destructive thermodynamic event. It is a blowing up, a flying apart process; it is a breaking up or down process; it is an "expanding" descent from "order" to chaos, from hot to cold. According to the laws of thermodynamics we should be going from efficiency to inefficiency, leading to a dying universe. (I am not saying the laws of thermodynamics don't apply; they just don't apply to the initial process of creation.)

But what process am I really describing? Behold, a creation made of an endless procession of wonders. Not a universe breaking down, but one coming together, unfolding logically from one principle into another—hydrogen becoming stars, and stars giving light as they change their hydrogen fuel into the heavier elements, the substance of which planets and living things here on earth are made. And before hydrogen? A similar process of unfolding, creating the tiniest particles, the building blocks of the elements themselves, and all following a pattern formed out of an initial, orderly, creative principle, rather than a destructive, chaotic event.

THE "BIG BANG" TIME PROBLEM

The problem of time is twofold. First, for a Big Bang creation event to happen, time would have to precede the event. The question is: How does it do that? What is the dynamic that would cause the existence of time before any creation event? Scientists are not clear on this question. They have another problem with time. In their concept of a Big Bang creation event, the Bang would cause time "wind" to ripple or blow in an *outward* motion from the center of the explosion. In other words, although omnidirectional from a center frame of reference, from our point of view time would have to be consistently one-directional. And yet, I believe I can show time as a consistently *omnidirectional* wind, meaning it comes from all directions at once—the effect being that time predictably slows down as we move in any particular direction.

If the Big Bang model were true, the effect on time would be quite different. The reason is that if time were one-directional, and you were driving with the time "wind" in the same direction, time would begin to slow down as you caught up with the time wind. However, if you traveled in the opposite direction towards the "Big Bang center," then the time wind would have to "blow harder" against you, and hence time would move faster, relative to you. This does not happen. A clock ticks consistently slower in every direction that one chooses to travel through space. Therefore, time cannot be one-directional.

Furthermore, how can we explain a Big Bang creation event without time preceding it? Events can happen only in time. Were there no time, there could be no procession of causes and effects. For a Big Bang to occur, time had to precede the event—and that's impossible. Why? Because even if it did exist before the explosion, how could time escape the phenomenal gravity that would inevitably result from such an inexplicably dense mass—so dense, in fact, that it is not really "mass" as we know it?

Consider the mind-boggling gravity of a black hole, believed to be a star collapsed in on itself; this pales by comparison to the "original" density we are discussing. And yet, a black hole is supposed to be mass of such inconceivable density and compression that a teaspoon of such matter might weigh five million tons on earth. Its gravity is so powerful that everything—matter, light, *even time itself*—gets sucked in, disappearing down a drain hole where all known laws of science cease, and nothing more happens.

But no matter how dense a black hole might be (and they say there are quasars that can swallow whole galaxies), nothing that we know of could possibly compare with the gravitational pull of that mythical, original singularity that supposedly caused the Big Bang. What physicists describe as infinitely hot, infinitely compressed, infinitely dense, unimaginably small, etc., this pre-bang density would have a gravity of such magnitude that nothing could possibly escape it, not even time. What "pushing out" force can overcome such a "pulling in" gravity?

Of course, all this theorizing ignores the simple question: Who or what created the original density? Something already created certainly can't be called a creation event. Clearly they are saying that the universe had a beginning; but then by all logic, it should have a Beginner, an uncreated Creator. After all, the laws of science are profoundly suggestive of an ordering Mind. And yet science keeps leaving Him out of the event by starting the universe with an already existing "lump." Is the "lump" itself to be considered the Prime Mover of all existence and maker of the laws thereof? Can you seriously imagine all the profound complexities of the universe coming from a mindless lump?

UNIVERSAL GEOMETRY OF MOTION AND STILLNESS

This book is about creation through an energy field scintillating in the darkness, creation out of what appears to be a nothing before time began. Black holes are not necessarily destructive; rather, they may be expressions of creation happening billions of years ago, witnessed now through our telescopes. Creation, I say, is a geometric symphony, an endless variation of motions and stillnesses. Here, the word *nothing* is quite precise, because matter is composed of an extra-dimensional no-thing, yet-to-be things.

The key principle presented here is that matter and the progression of matter are made of an unrolling variation of one geometrical theme—original motion and stillness (energy and the apparent absence of energy). While motion can exist only with a relative stillness to define it, *perfect* creation stillness is able to exist without motion; all other "stillnesses" are relative stillnesses, which is to say they are in motion. All the building blocks of nature have some kind of nucleus-center that is relatively still compared with the motions around it. Just as these relatively still "centers" are essential for the existence of matter, so is a perfect inertial center also essential for the existence of the whole universe.

If the universe is in motion (and we know it is), then there must be an absolute rest to define that motion. This absolute stillness surrounded by the "all" of absolute motion establishes a pattern followed by the rest of the universal building blocks, from atoms to planets. Atoms and planets involve *relative* motions with *relative* stillnesses at their centers; however, in the case of the creation event, this still center is not relative but must be a pivotal point of absolute rest—The Absolute Rest Center—the unmoved Mover of all things that are created and that move.

Can a solar system exist as a complete whole without a central and (relatively) still sun? Would it remain a solar system? Obviously not. Can wheels turn without an axle? Can atoms exist without their nuclei? Would they remain atoms? No, they would be reduced to something less than themselves. Everything orbits, circumorbits, cycles, or circles around some kind of center-event-cause. Even plants and other living things revolve in life and death cycles.

Can you think of anything in your life, or in this universe, that doesn't involve such a system? Even man's life ought to revolve around, and be centered in, his Creator. The redeemed, spiritually in-breathed man (God-centered) manifests the ultimate physical and metaphysical cycle, the living, breathing poetry of ultimate motion and rest.

The question once again is, can the universe, in absolute motion, exist without an absolute inertial rest to define it? In the context of Einstein's theory, the answer is no, for in his view nothing can be considered to be in motion unless it's compared to something relatively at rest.

Plato said that time and the succession of change is the moving image of eternity according to number. The absolute place of Universal Stillness, which gave birth to Original Motion, is the model from which all relative motions and relative stillnesses derive. Without these centers of relative stillness defining the motions that become the geometric progression called creation (a universe made of an infinite variety of interconnecting, spinning, orbiting, circumorbiting balls), there could be no creation.

THE GEOMETRY OF ONE

The ancient Greek mathematician Pythagoras maintained that "one" is not a number, but the underlying continuum initially containing and giving birth to all numbers. And that "one" is the underlying unity and starting point for all systems, the root nature of all things, ourselves, the earth, and the universe.

Modern science confirms his mathematics of creation. Of what, may we ask, are the elements comprised? Numbers, atomic numbers. A hydrogen atom differs in properties from a lead atom only because its nuclear properties differ, meaning the number of "moons" (electrons) that are circumorbiting an equivalently numbered, but differently charged nucleus. The essences themselves aren't different, only their charge and their numbers.

The energy essence that makes up the electrons of the hydrogen atom is the same as the essence of those of the lead atom—electrons are electrons in both. And the same with the protons and neutrons in the nucleus. It is only the numbers that change the properties of the respective elements, giving them spectacular new forms and functions, from the giant redwood tree to a sparkling diamond. What I am saying is that from the first "One" in the beginning, everything is everything else in a *creation symphony*, a geometry of never-ending, complex, orbiting numbers— just as Pythagoras's never-ending complexity of numbers developed out of the simplicity of one. It is the geometric growth of one added to itself, and so on, in a spectacular creative flow—and not a "bang" produced by a lump.

Two

BIG BANG WITH A NEW TWIST
THE TIMEWIND THEORY OF THE UNIVERSE

*"We shall find in what follows that the velocity
of light in our theory plays the role, physically,
of an infinitely greater velocity."*

Albert Einstein, 1905

Why am I so concerned with the subject of time? Simple. We are born mortal, subject to the ravages of time, change, and decay of body and even soul. I knew intuitively as a boy that there was something odd about death, that inevitable, desperate end to life. As natural as it is, I could see that death was also somehow *unnatural*.

Time has become our master, and what a hard master it is. We have a brief opportunity, a certain amount of time to rediscover the secret of transcending time, how the soul of man can live in the time-bound world, yet not be subject to it.

The doorway out is also the doorway in—call it the Alpha-Omega point. There exists at the event horizon of creation this placeless, other-dimensional "place" at the center of the universe where God spoke, and *still speaks* His creation into existence. He is there at the spiritual door of material creation, and He is also within us, standing in silent witness to it all. But more, His miraculous creation is not a thing separate from science; it is *science itself*, a system of expression that flows naturally out of principles we can understand. Unlike a "Big Bang" chaotic explosive event which bears no relation to us, I am describing a creative flow we can recognize because the same principles that made the universe made us. This creation event is not something foreign we have to "believe in," but something familiar we can spiritually and logically "behold." And beholding His creation, we are meant to live in awe and wonder, and in ever-increasing faith.

For this, God not only rewards us with His indwelling eternal love and guidance, but when at last we have lived our lives, when we have been fully formed in his image, having been remolded through our minds from within, He imparts the secret of time transcendence. None who have received this salvation can ever utter a word of explanation. The mystery goes with them, leaving the rest of humanity behind, either to perish or to find the truth that will set them free.

Every discovery, revelation, and insight is a "growing through going" toward that marvelous eternal moment. What better way to come to the end of our time than to comprehend its beginning? For in those realizations, we shall see both the beginning and the end. For where the end is, there is also our new beginning—with the Beginner. Whoever has ears to hear this, let him understand it. I will do my best to make it clear in these pages.

THE TIMEWIND THEORY

Sir Isaac Newton claimed that time flows. Many modern physicists dispute this belief, but let me demonstrate its logic. Consider the following example which suggests that time is not still (and therefore must flow in some way).

It is a warm sunny day, not a cloud in the sky. The air is dead calm. You climb into your convertible, and as you accelerate to 60 miles per hour, a 60 mph wind blows in your face. Of course, the faster you drive the stronger the wind. If this "wind" were instead the space/time medium, you would think that time itself would act the same way, passing or "blowing" more quickly as you accelerate through it. But oddly enough, it does just the opposite: Time actually slows down the faster you travel through it.

Now let's use a different example to understand the behavior of time. Let's say you go for a drive again and this time it's a windy day, blowing steadily at 60 mph. What happens when you accelerate going in the same direction as the wind? It's obvious; the wind appears to slow down, and when your car reaches 60 mph, the wind no longer exists for you—just dead calm. Of course, for everyone else the wind is still blowing. This is more like what the time "wind" is doing, which seems to suggest that time has some sort of velocity, a motion, a "wind." The faster you move through it, the slower time moves, until time comes to a dead stop (theoretically speaking, if you could travel fast enough). If this could happen, time would cease to exist for you, but it would still be "blowing"—or passing—for the rest of creation.

What this demonstrates is that time must be moving in some fashion because if you travel in any direction, it slows down. The fact that time slows down no matter which way you go, suggests that time must be omnidirectional. So how, scientists will no doubt ask, could a time "wind" blow in every direction and still be a wind? After all, with ordinary wind, you can't have two winds blowing in opposing directions at once, can you? They would surely cancel each other out. The other question you might ask is that if they are somehow able to move through each other without canceling each other out, which wind causes the "time slowing" phenomenon? These questions will be answered in later chapters of this book.

Despite the many important questions concerning an omnidi-rectional wind, one thing is sure: There are far greater problems with a theory that depends on a moving, "unidirectional time." Remember, in the big "hot" bang theory, scientists present time as proceeding from a central "Big Bang" explosion, that is, in one "outward" direction. Conversely it has been theorized by the eminent physicist Stephen Hawking that time stretching out in one direction may well eventually collapse back, making time run backward—again in one direction, toward a singularity center. But either way, out or back, according to this theory time must move, and move in one direction as we experience it. However, it seems that based on accepted behavior of time, this can't be so—for no matter what direction we go, time slows down. Thus, time must be omnidirectional.

BEYOND PHYSICS

We are not dealing here just with proven mechanical laws, Einsteinian concepts, or with quantum physics. We are dealing here with forces far beyond even light velocities—"millions" of times greater.

Unlike winds or rivers, which if coming from opposite directions would clash and neutralize each other's forces, time "wind" actually moves through itself—because time isn't matter. Air is matter; water is matter. But time has a spirit-like quality and is able to permeate matter as well as to move through itself. Even in the deepest coal mine, time is passing, causing change.

Compare time with two phantom railroad trains, coming down the same track and passing through one another as though neither existed, continuing in their respective directions unaffected. I know that it may be difficult for many people to imagine time as a form of velocity or a motion; after all, by what "time" would you measure such motion? We don't think of air as wind unless it blows enough to enable us to see or feel its evidence, as ocean waves, or leaves falling off trees. But we do feel time passing and we do see change and decay. However, if we were to travel at the same speed as that timewind, time would be dead still for us—because we could no longer experience it as "wind." In other words, if we traveled at the same speed as the motion of time, we would feel a personal timelessness. But it would not be true timelessness, since it would still be part of a moving time continuum, revolving around the true timeless center.

BIG BANG AS EXPANDING TIME "STRINGS"

To grasp this concept of timeless motion (actual motion without the need for time), visualize the fashioning of a ball of string. Begin slowly, winding the string, representing the time flow around and from the center of the universe. Observe how the string flows, circumorbiting (in every direction), shaping itself into a three-dimensional ball, growing in volume as the string moves out with increasing velocity.

This energy phenomenon is strikingly different from the energy profile of the Big Bang theory in that this energy is slower toward the center, and greater in expansion, while any normal explosion creates just the opposite effect. Even more fascinating is the fact that a steady state of acceleration is a prelude to the creation of gravity and matter, as you will presently see.

This basically represents a new model of the universe, beginning with a calm inertial center, flowing out, faster and faster, forming the expanding space curve threshold of the universe. Scientists may well be correct in claiming that the universe is expanding outwardly—but, as I said before, not from a hot-bang explosive center. In my "time string" model of the universe, we do not start with matter; instead we begin with a force I call pre-time (yet-to-be-time) which causes matter to "clot" out of it. Of course, the new matter cannot keep up, and thus drags back in what becomes time to that new matter.

It is not that the explosion theory of Big Bang is wrong, but rather that it is not truly an explosion; it only duplicates the *effect* of a "bang" as we experience it. You might say it begins with a "whoosh" and ends with a "bang." At the center, it starts out slowly but expands so rapidly, causing an instant unfolding of creation, that we experience it as an explosive bang. After all, what is an explosion but a rapid expansion? All that is being described here is a different kind of rapid expansion, one based on a steady state acceleration, a "gravity" force preceding the clotting of matter and then acting upon it.

To fully understand how time comes into existence with regard to matter, we need to use the example of our automobile driving 60 mph with a 60 mph wind, and therefore experiencing no wind. As the car slows down, the wind becomes apparent. In the same way, as original matter clots out of the pre-time primordial wind and slows down, the force that made it becomes a wind to it, experienced as time. Conversely, if matter could move as fast as pre-time force, there would be no apparent time; not only would there be no time at that point, there would be no space and hence no room for matter. Matter would cease to exist. Thankfully, matter cannot go as fast as timewind. In summation, time (and time/space/distance) exist only if timewind "passes" matter.

MASS EXPERIENCES PRE-TIME FORCE AS TIMEWIND

If timewind moves and expands in string-like fashion, there needs to be some prime-moving force, itself unmoved. This force is the absolute "nuclear" stillness, the no-thing from which pre-time force comes. Pre-time force is the force that is pushed into matter and unfolds as creation, all bathed in a timewind of space/time flowing in its perpetually orbiting motion around the still center (like the string forming the ball).

The primal force that flings the timewind out centrifugally

literally compresses matter into existence, causing minute particles to fall out of the storm of motion at the periphery of the universe, which could be called another creation event horizon. The very pressure of this phenomenal force causes a clotting, a spinning of primordial energy around itself that manifests as the first subatomic particles, which I call "origitrons."

So we have pre-time force, and then we have matter clotting out of it, which, being "heavier," lags in the pre-time force, allowing it to experience the current of the pre-time force from which it has fallen as a kind of wind that we call time. Time, then, is that timewind from the perspective of mass; as Einstein might have said, it is relative to mass.

What we created beings experience as time begins as that pre-time force, flowing from a timeless place, circumorbiting (spinning out in every direction) from an inertial rest center or creation event. And so, what we experience as time flowing over us also happens to be the essence of matter, resulting in the flowing space/time/distance with respect to mass as mass clumps and appears. A more detailed account of how time becomes matter/space/time/distance will be given later.

Because pre-time force (which manifests as time to mass) is a primordial "essence," it can both cause motion and resist motion in every direction uniformly, and thus impose speed limits on light and matter in every direction uniformly. In this way, pre-time force regulates the crucial relationship between light and matter. In other words, it tells light how fast to move and gives matter its range of motion.

UNIVERSAL SPEED LIMITS

Anyone with boating experience knows that the speed of a displacement vessel cutting through the ocean is limited by both the design and the length of the hull. However, no matter how well the vessel is crafted, the hull speed is regulated by the inherent drag of the water. At a certain point, the ocean imposes a "speed limit" that cannot be exceeded. Regardless of how powerful your engine is, the "whole ocean" ultimately resists you. If you could build an engine powerful enough to push that boat against the "whole ocean," you may as well be pushing it up against an infinitely solid wall. The hull would be crushed flat. This is precisely what would happen to any spaceship with enough power to push the ship against the inherent resistance of the "whole ocean" of the space/time ether.

The idea that there is resistance in space contradicts current scientific belief, which claims there is no space ether, just a void, and thus nothing present to resist motion. But if such is the case, how can that which is nothing end up resisting? For we are told, and I agree, that matter cannot approach light speed. Science cannot see what space really is because space consists of primal forces that are as much of another dimension as they are of this one. Our best chance to know these forces is by analyzing their effect on observable primal forms of matter. Thus, something must be doing the resisting; otherwise, matter could reach light speed and go beyond. We know that light is limited to a speed of 186,000.272 mps but we don't know why. I propose that light is limited in speed because it is regulated by something in the universe that resists it everywhere, including in space, which is not a void. The more exciting part of this reality is that light is not just regulated by this force, but *energized* by it. Perhaps an example will help.

Consider a log in a river being pushed by the current. Could it also be resisting motion? The answer is yes; it resists the current and it is also being pushed along by the current. If one were to take away the landscape and the river, and make them invisible, and then take away the earth itself and just leave the log and the force pushing the log, what would you see? You would see the log moving through space forever—but you wouldn't see what was pushing it. Substitute our subatomic "origitron" particle for the log and what you have is a particle of "light" moving at 186,000.272 mps pushed by the timewind (with a little drag resistance) just like that log in the river. In a similar way, timewind is pushing all the planets and stars and sustaining them around a universal axis in their various motions and orbits, keeping atoms and electrons spinning in what appears to be perpetual motion. Just as leaves are lighter than logs, and move faster in the river current, so does light move faster than matter along the ether wind "strings" of time. Light obeys the law of time in its realm and matter obeys the law of time in its realm. Matter drags and cannot move as fast as light in time, nor can light go as slowly as matter in time. Each obeys the timewind law that rules its particular form.

I am trying to build a context for an essentially simple point. I would like to advise the reader to return to this chapter for a second reading, when I believe it will become clearer.

INVISIBLE STRINGS AT WORK

The invisible strings of timewind force, expanding and circumorbiting from a timeless center with immeasurable velocity, originate from an absolutely calm universal center, or creation event. This may seem like a contradiction in terms, but part of what I am saying in this book is that there has to be a calm for a creation event to happen; there must be an absolute rest or there can be no motion of any kind.

"Time strings" (the perpetual tracks of the pre-time force) shape an expanding, three-dimensional, spherical universe causing an invisible, curved horizon boundary. That fairly well describes pre-time's behavior as it swirls out from a timeless, inertial, creation event center. It is slower at the "eye" entrance to the universe and expands circumorbitally around its creation event center, producing "pre-time strings" of force, whirling outward, filling space with time (with respect to mass) in every possible direction, for without mass, space/time is unthinkable. So before mass there is pre-time force which, upon the creation of mass, becomes perceptible as "wind" which herein is called timewind or time or space/time.

I want you to understand that time is not what you might think it to be; I am using "time" as the closest relative to what I call pre-time force which is not yet time but is itself the origin of time. Those "time strings" I have mentioned are not time itself but are the super-velocity "pathways" of pre-existent energy (pre-time force).

If you could make "time" visible and if you could stand on the pathway of one of the "orbiting pre-time strings," with what is now time rushing towards you like a wind blowing in your face, you would find something very interesting happening at the same instant—something that is a key to the riddle of existence. There would be *another* timewind also pushing you *from behind*. Although time, like those phantom trains coming from opposite directions, has no real effect on itself, it does affect an object in space with pressure on both (actually all) sides, maintaining whatever inertia (its relative motion or stillness) it already has. It is only when an object is mechanically propelled toward light velocity that it meets the physical/metaphysical resistance of the opposing timewind current, and consequently also of the whole universe behind it (just as the "whole ocean" potentially resists a boat). Simply put, the metaphysical dimension becomes physical when sufficient force and velocity are applied.

With respect to matter, timewind as a pushing force has little profound effect until mass begins to approach light velocity. At that point, timewind acts on mass like an increasingly irresistible regulator, exerting more and more pressure as mass is pushed toward light velocity, and finally, timewind becomes a cosmic other-dimensional "brick wall." Just as that displacement vessel in the ocean cannot exceed the speed limit set by the medium of the ocean, neither can mass overcome the universal power of pre-time force.

The pre-time force has a simple but all-pervasive effect on all things in the universe. The most obvious one is on the lightest of mass forms—subatomic particles which in their primitive mass form are carried along the timewind at full light speed. Mass is less affected for the obvious reason that it is much "heavier," as I mentioned. However, the key to understanding this phenomenon is to know that pre-time force is both a wind and a counter-wind; it is both a pushing and resisting force which manifests in different ways depending on the density (geometry) it encounters.

Light is affected by the "pushing wind," but at the same time it is also limited by the resisting wind. This phenomenon is most apparent in the lightest of particles, but the principle affects heavier mass as well. The problem here lies in the fact that the "pushing wind" cannot accelerate true mass, which must be propelled by its own source of energy. But this fact does not negate the principle of the resisting timewind which still acts on mass pushed toward light velocity. At that point, the resisting force is intolerant of that acceleration and acts like a barrier.

Three

THE COSMOLOGY OF MOVING STILLNESS

*"Give me motion and extension
and I will construct the universe."*

Descartes

E instein believed the velocity of light is the only constant in the universe. However, it would seem that if there is constant motion, there must also be a motionless constant. Just as time exists, so must there be a Timeless Origin of time. No motion without rest; no time without the Timeless.

Surrounding the creation event center of the universe there is nothing but darkness. Pre-time has yet to give form to energy and matter, through time in space. Near the center, time moves too slowly for any of the laws of science to exist before creation. And so there is "darkness on the face of the deep." Origin is like a black hole, wherein all that is to be is not yet.

Time, energy, and matter come swirling from the creation event, out of "nothing" into existence. Certain black holes, on the other hand, are gravitational in that they reverse the creation process, swirling everything back down gravitational vortices, compressing all into masses of "infinite" density, with their singularities receding back full circle into the unknowable dimension. It is a universal breathing out and breathing in. Some black holes may return matter's essence back to whence it came, renewing and recycling creation, pointing the way back full circle to the beginning of our physical universe. Hopefully our souls will also find the way to a new beginning, but through a different door.

MOTION IS IMPOSSIBLE WITHOUT STILLNESS

You are sitting quietly in your house and everything is perfectly still. You awaken to greet the morning sun as it rises, and observe it coursing through the heavens until it sets at dusk. Relative to your point of view, you are still while the sun rises and sets around you. And this is a fact; from your frame of reference the sun really does revolve around you. However, things are not always what they appear to be. There is yet another relative truth. From the vantage point of outer space, you would observe your house rotating along with the planet, as well as orbiting about a still central sun. Each stillness is a relative one and ceases to be still from a different perspective.

Everything that is relatively still is actually moving through time and space in cycles, orbits, and circles. Further out in the universe, even our "still" sun is seen to be in motion, relative to other heavenly bodies that appear to be still—and yet, are not. This relationship of motion and apparent stillness goes on *ad infinitum*.

Therefore, absolutely nothing is truly still. The whole of the universe is in motion. And yet, any one of the various motions in the universe may be observed to be motion only when compared to what is moving slower, relatively at rest. Yet we know that every "rest" which defines motion is itself in motion. Only by whatever is relatively at rest can we know for sure that motion itself actually exists. So then by what means do we know that the whole universe is in motion? Enlightened reason is required to answer this question.

Motion is defined and even made possible by its relativity to a lesser motion. I repeat, motion is identified in only one way, by its relativity to a lesser motion—the one that we perceive to be still. Without a progression of relative stillnesses, none of the individual motions would have the particular kind of activity responsible for its very nature, its field effect, the very function of chemistry assigned to its particular geometrical matter form. All would be still. In fact, the procession of motions would become a procession of stillnesses.

This is not a play on words. We are dealing with a serious reality here, so let me rephrase it: Motion cannot be said to be in motion without a comparative stillness to confirm it, and more often than not to compel it to exist. It is only because of all those relative motions and rests that we can know for sure that any motion exists at all. By way of that procession of motions and stillnesses, from the beginning, cause leading to effect and effect becoming the cause of more effects, we know that the whole universe is moving, with every "stillness" moving. That much we know in principle, as well as in fact.

While we cannot observe all these various stillnesses for ourselves, we can observe the principle and know it to be true, even at the furthermost reaches of the cosmos where we can never go. The whole theory of the missing Relative rests upon an observable principle that is understandable and immutable. From this kind of principle, we can calculate the whole and see it as if we had an other-dimensional telescope. The beauty of observable principle as opposed to observable "facts" is that observing principle gives us a "far sight" that telescopes don't have.

It is clear that what makes relative motions in the universe possible is their various companions—all their relative stillnesses. It is never the other way around. Since we've indicated that the whole universe is perceived to be in motion, the conclusion is inescapable; there absolutely, incontrovertibly must be an absolute rest, a Mover Unmoved that makes possible the absolute motion of the whole universe. If all the other motions need to be defined by relative rest, why shouldn't the whole universe need an absolute rest, an Ultimate Relative, to define and to "speak" into existence the absoluteness of universal motion?

Without that Absolute Stillness, there could be no prime mover of all that is moving, and the absolute motion of the whole universe could be considered to be the very stillness itself. Remember, we do know by virtue of relativity (of stillness in motion and motion in stillness) that indeed the universe is absolutely in motion, and that there can be no motion imputed without respect to something still—in this case, without the Still Mover, Himself unmoved, speaking motion into existence as if to say "Let there be."

While absolute stillness can and does exist without motion, the converse is impossible: Absolute motion cannot exist without absolute rest. Take away what is central in anything, and everything will begin to collapse and fold back into the pre-beginning, the non-existence of matter before creation.

We know from this construction that there must be at least two absolutes: One is that the whole universe is absolutely moving (science accepts this fact), and the other is that there must be an absolute stillness to let it all happen, to speak all of motion into existence. This absolute stillness is creation's absolute Relative. So we can realize now that there are at least two absolutes in the universe, the One absolutely at rest, and the other in absolute motion. Rest imputes motion, both in motion's origin and in all its later manifestations.

PRE-TIME: THE ESSENCE OF MATTER

The energy swirling out of the "eye of the hurricane" creation event is what I have called pre-time force, and this force is really the "All" of Creation, everything becoming everything else, the totality of motion we discussed. It is also the leading edge of what we know as time. Its "velocity" is millions, if not billions, of times faster than that of light.

This "timeless" energy is the leading edge of "pre-time," sweeping the universe. It is somewhat like the glowing sweep on a radar screen. As the luminous radar arm sweeps around and around, it outlines its target, leaving behind a trail of little phosphorescent blips. To get a glimpse of how the pre-time force creates matter, think of tiny particles falling out of the sweeping edge of pre-time force like those blips on the radar screen.

Just as the phosphorescence, trailing the luminous arm, is reinforced with each sweep, so are the particles dropping out of the pre-time, timeless arm leaving behind subatomic spinning "fire balls" (pre-mass) in the wake of what now becomes the "time wind"—time as we know it.

Let me be clear. That sweeping pre-time motion extending from the creation center is not actually time. It becomes time to the particles falling behind in its wake, which are sustained with every pass of the radar-like arm sweeping the universe that I call pre-time force. Have you ever asked yourself what keeps electrons spinning around their nucleus? Science doesn't know. But just as the basketball spinning on a fingertip needs its spin to be reinforced constantly to maintain that spin, so is the universe, electrons and all, alive with God's constant reinforcing hand. "If I should withhold my hand, sayeth the Lord, all things would vanish."

TIMELESS BUT NOT MOTIONLESS

The true timeless/motionless realm exists only in the still origin/center of the universe. However, the motion of the pre-time, radar-like arm extending from the creation event is timeless as far as matter is concerned. Time for us does not exist along the "leading edge" of that "arm" any more than wind does when you are moving in the same direction and at the same speed as the wind. This timeless motion is not only prephysical, but it is where a super pressure is developed—needed to clump primordial energy into mass. As with any centrifugal phenomenon, the force at the outer edges experiences greater stress. Just like the famous "whip" in ice skating or roller skating, the person on the outside has a very difficult time hanging on to the rest of the line of skaters, and inevitably flies off to the side, unable to hold on.

To reiterate, along this pre-time line of force there exists no time for anything; it is pure timeless motion. It is timeless but not motionless—timeless in the sense that if it were possible (and it isn't) to ride along its leading edge, you would be still while in "motion." You wouldn't be able to move. There would be no space to move in. You would feel no motion; no time would be passing, no wind would be blowing over you as real time. Nothing could happen because there would be no matter, no time, no space in which anything could take place. However, there would be something—a realm not of this physical world, a realm in which spirit dwells but flesh (or matter) cannot live. In this dimension pre-time force flows as metaphysical motion in a timeless eternity where spirits can move and have their being.

The Timeless God is the Prime Mover of this pre-time force that extends out and emanates from His timeless Center. He is the primordial power from which everything takes shape. Like computer combinations of ones and zeros, motion and rest crescendo through time and space in endless, expanding combinations and geometric forms, becoming the different components of matter.

MATTER AS "FROZEN" MOTION IN THE RIVER OF TIME

Just as flowing water freezes into a solid, so too does flowing pre-time motion become "solid" in the form of what we shall call origitrons. Pre-time motion is transformed—or "clotted"—into these smallest of all "light" particles (not yet the more complex form of solar light with which we are familiar). These original "frozen" clumps of pre-time motion, little "fiery" whirlpools, form the first stage of larger entities by circumorbiting one another without a nucleus, but simply around a relatively still space.

This is the basic sequence of creative events: The Still Timeless God gave birth to motion. Motion clots into original subatomic mass, dragging back in the time wind to become those smallest of all particles, origitrons. In the course of events, the origitrons, in turn, come together as those larger entities described above, naturally evolving into ever more complex arrangements which we know as electrons, atoms, and molecules, complete with their relatively still centers.

Thus an orderly sequence of events is set in motion, resulting in what we behold as creation. And this creation continues and never ends, for God is a Creator who never ceases. The Creation we usually think of as a "past event" is actually going on now, just as it did in the beginning. For in God there is no past, there is no future; there is only the everpresent now where we ourselves must live.

Four

THE THIRD LAW OF MOTION—TIME

*"If they ask you, 'What is the sign
of the Father in you?' say to them,
'It is movement and repose.'"*

Gospel of Thomas

The whole of the created universe connects to the pivot of origin, the inertial hub, the "eye of the hurricane" of creation. In this way, the ever-presence of God pervades His universe. Pre-time force (time, motion) flows out from the still beginning, circumorbiting that center with centrifugal gravity (or anti-gravity, possibly Einstein's Cosmological Constant). It is centrifugal in the sense that things are created by being flung out. So instead of a "Big Bang," we have a quiet, steady, continuing source of creation, and a rotating, expanding universe, continually dependent on a steady flow of pre-time force from the center. Around the hub or eye of creation flows the universe in motion, continually giving birth to mass, and evolving that mass in motion through time.

Einstein believed that true science was naturally simple and beautiful, unfolding in a logical order. That is what time is, simple and beautiful. It is a key relative which rules over physics as a third law of motion, as you will see. Remember that the whole universe is a symphony of relative motions and stillnesses.

Time is motion. Time involves the motion of mass through space. When you retire for the night and awaken to greet the dawn, you are certainly not at the same place you were when you fell asleep. You will have traveled at least 80,000 miles.

If the whole universe could stop, if all its matter motions were suddenly frozen, do you think time would exist? It would not.

But neither would matter exist. Matter cannot exist without time, and time cannot exist without matter, as you will presently see.

Time passes and makes existence possible, causing succession and change that we call evolution. Time can never be still, and the fact that it "passes" reinforces existence. As I said, if time suddenly ceased, nothing would exist; all matter would dematerialize instantly into the no-thing from which it came (the pre-time wind). Furthermore, for even that to happen the pre-time river of life itself would have to stop at its fount of eternal stillness.

Time is mass in motion through yet another motion. And that motion is the pre-time force of the ether wind. There are two motions here, one within the other.

Time is like a grain of sand pushed along in a river. The immediate current flowing over (and touching) the sand is time, and the continuing river flow is infinite distance—relative to that grain of sand. Distance is created by the motion of the river flowing over the moving grain of sand. The river itself never stops flowing ahead of the little grain of sand.

Now consider those two motions again, bearing in mind that this analogy is only a two-dimensional model. The first motion is the current of the river, and the second is the movement of the grain of sand as pushed along by the current. The grain of sand, never able by its own energy to catch up to the endless flow of water, continues to be pushed along, covering much distance but, in a manner of speaking, never arriving anywhere.

Let us use this analogy to make another point, which is that the river current, pushing that grain of sand, exerts a certain pressure upon it. Likewise, time (to matter in space) exerts a pressure on mass. Mass is bathed in and pushed by a mysterious "background" pre-time force, an eternal, multidimensional river subtly flowing over everything.

Keep in mind that this subtle "ether," this pre-time force,

does not merely pass over us as time; it also exerts a pressure on matter. While it is the current that exerts the pressure on sand, it is the shaping around the sand or pebble that we know as time. One might say, then, that time is a form of the ether current relative to the size of mass and the swiftness of the flow of pre-time force. But the "shaping" or curving is not only time as it passes over mass, it is also a pressure upon it.

If you drop a pebble in a stream, the moment the pebble hits the water it has a relationship with the water that wasn't there before. At one and the same moment, the current immediately wraps around the pebble and exerts a pressure on it. The "wrapping around" is analogous to time, and what is then time to the pebble exerts a pressure upon it. Pre-time force is time, is pressure, is gravity. This is a new concept of gravity, the behavior of which is understood, but not its real cause. Modern science considers gravity a property of mass, a pulling force, but I say gravity is a pushing force directly connected to the phenomenon of time. This will be covered in later chapters.

Remember, the movement of the grain of sand in the faster flowing river represents two forms of motion, one within the other: one, the motion of the flowing river (the elusive ether) and two, all the movements of matter in the river because the river is moving.

By now you may be wondering why I say that time is the third law of motion. Consider what is matter. Matter consists of atoms, each composed of spinning, swirling little fireballs of energy, moving internally at light velocity. Thus, there are three motions: In the order of creation, the first is the pre-time force, flowing as the current of a river; the second motion is the same force of the current, swirling into eddies that we call matter (establishing the spinning nature of matter); and the third motion is that same current which has formed those swirls, now flowing past matter as time, leaving matter dragging in the force of the current to create the effect of space/time/distance. It is the dragging of matter in the river current that creates a relationship between the mass that is dragging and the river that flows on into infinity. It is the flow of the river that represents distance, but without matter the concept of distance is meaningless.

Space/time requires a matter relationship—without matter there would only be the flow. Indeed, space/time is unthinkable without the presence of matter to give meaning to time flowing into distance. To illustrate the point further, the faster one accelerates matter, the more distance disappears and the slower time runs. This is because distance is represented by what is flowing over and beyond us. And so, if you could speed up equal to the current, then the two motions would become one—hence, no more space, time, or distance. Space/time is the contrast between one motion and the other; in fact, it is the critical difference between one motion and the other.

Consider light: If light were not "told" how slow to move by the resistance of the pre-time wind, it would "reach infinity." This would be useless energy because it goes on to endless nowhere. Light, matter, and space/time all exist by way of their discreet limits, their relative slownesses. Therefore, as one endless motion, creation would remain unbirthed. The Divine Intelligence behind the energy of infinite motion gave birth to the universe by causing finite motion, the effects and causes of lesser motions relative to one another. All these motions rest in the Unmoved Timeless Self, the Master of time.

TIME: THE MASTER REGULATOR OF CREATION

Time is the master controller, regulator of local reality. All the laws of physics and of nature are geared to the way time passes. Time can pass faster or slower, depending upon the varying motions of mass through the ether wind. It should be noted that time itself is produced; it is the effect of an other-dimensional causative factor. But in this dimension time is the governing phenomenon, a change agent in the order of creation.

As matter clumps and spins out of the ether wind which is that pre-time, pre-physical flowing energy field—poof!—time appears instantly along with matter; that very same force that gave birth to matter now flows around it as a time/pressure.

Let me approach this in a different way. Consider a canoe as it drifts down a river with the current flowing past the canoe. If your hat fell into the river, it would shoot forward away from you, carried off by the current. Matter is the canoe; time is the river; the increasing space between the hat and the boat represents the flowing of time into infinity. Just as the canoe can be paddled to catch up to the hat, as we move faster through space, distance would become shorter and time would slow down. If you will ponder this illustration, you will note that space/time's distance is affected by the increased motion of matter through the ether wind.

Surely you can see that time is that relationship between two motions, the background flow and matter in motion, as it drags in pre-time force. Therefore, if you were to steady-state accelerate mass, it would be squeezed into smaller and smaller space/time, whereby the laws of physics are governed proportionately by a slower space/time. In other words, as matter moves faster, time squeezes and slows down.

Therefore the motion of mass through the ether wind tells time how to adjust the laws governing matter with respect to its velocity. What acceleration does is compress time; as time is compressed it affects the dynamic of all the laws of physics relative to the particular motion of the mass.

What we experience as time is something like the bow wave, because the ether curves as it flows around mass, quite in the way the bow wave of a ship causes the compression of the ocean against the hull. Just as the ocean's resistance transmits a pressure to the ship through its bow wave, so does a gravitational compression time wave adjust the laws of physics with respect to the motion of mass in a steady state of acceleration (see glossary). And as I will show later, this kind of time pressure acts in a similar way on a massive presence in space, precisely Einstein's Equivalence Principle pertaining to gravity.

Time, therefore, may be considered as a folded, curved form of pre-time, a different form of the original force just as the atomic spinning nature of matter is also simply a different form of pre-time force.

Time, matter, and the pre-time force are three different aspects of an original expression. Since these three are essentially interrelated, theoretically one should be able to squeeze them together. Of course, it would take all the force in the universe to accomplish the job. This set aside, the faster one accelerates matter, the slower time goes, and the faster space/time disappears. Eventually, two of the motions, separate in creation, collapse back into the original motion, pre-time force, whence they came.

It is my opinion that one needs to go much faster than the speed of light for such an event to occur (for matter to dematerialize) even though one can hardly cause matter to approach the speed of light. Yet light itself would still exist with time flowing over it. Thus one would have to exert phenomenal pressure even on light in order for all of existence to be collapsed and extinguished.

Actually matter wouldn't really dematerialize. What would most likely happen is something like this: If you could push creation that fast, the downward pressure of steady state acceleration (gravity equivalent) would make matter so heavy it could become a black hole causing the pre-time force to go directly into it.

The master background wind, pre-time force, tells light how fast to move, and by limiting the range of the velocity of mass it tells time how slow to go.

TIME • PRESSURE • GRAVITY

Time is caused by the presence of mass in space that curves the timewind force flowing around it from every direction as a gravitational pressure, which is a push force, not a pull force as is currently believed. A massive presence in space does not need a steady state of acceleration to warp time and thus become a gravity. Its sheer volume and density has the effect of capturing the pre-time current from every direction as time/pressure/gravity.

Time, the master regulator of matter, is itself controlled by the pre-physical ether wind I call pre-time force.

As indicated earlier, if one were able to accelerate matter fast enough, the steady state pressure of the existing wind (time) would become so massive a gravitational pressure that the wind would no longer curve around it as time, but would compress directly into the now infinitely dense mass. A massive black hole might behave in the same way by virtue of its incomprehensible density—where time, space, and matter collapse and cease to exist as we know them. For the distance around mass would have the effect of a vacuum, sucking the pre-time wind energy into it. Of course, anything in the vicinity would be pulled into this tremendous vortex.

Toward the center of the universe, pre-time motion/force runs too slowly for anything to come into existence—except pre-time itself, running slowly. Remember, time is timewind only as measured by the existence of material things, and therefore in the pre-existence of mass there is no time. The wind of pre-time, on the other hand, circumorbits slower and slower the nearer it comes to the creation center of the universal hub. From the still creation event, outward toward the fury of pre-time creation, the center is in continuous connection with all things God has made.

THE "GOD BANG" AND STEADY STATE EXPLOSION

The whole pre-time energy of the universe is moving, although more slowly at the hub than at the periphery where matter is sustained. That seems to contradict the notion of pre-time as a constant. For the record, let me state that at the sustaining periphery of creation where pre-time is time, where matter is made possible and where all the planets float in space, time flows the same for all of us. But the fact that "time" should be slower toward the center of the universe does not contradict the notion of time as a constant. The reason for this is that where time slows, time isn't yet time. Why? Simply because matter hasn't yet clotted from it and there can be no time without matter. Thus pre-time moving too slowly doesn't create matter and remains pre-time, or latent creation.

Although pre-time is an accelerating force (Einstein's steady state), needed to gravitationally clot its energy into matter, it becomes a constant at the point of creation. This point of creation is not only where matter clots out of pre-time force, but this pressure point also represents the place where "honest time" exists—in other words, where a true time constant exists.

Where pre-time clots into matter, creating space/time, time exists and is here a constant. In fact, it could be said that creation of matter is the final point of the steady state acceleration of pre-time. Pre-time's relationship to matter at that point becomes a time constant. Again, creation exists instantly at the pressure point where steady state acceleration of pre-time energy attains its zenith of motion, just like any explosion where pressure builds to an explosive point. The difference is that this is not a "Big Bang" but a "God Bang," resulting in a flowing organic creation rather than explosive chaos. As matter is formed out of pre-time force, its relationship to pre-time changes; the same pre-time force that created matter now becomes time relative to matter. In case a question has arisen in the reader's mind, this dynamic of time will be further discussed in later chapters. Just remember that in this dimension time is indeed a constant; it is only the further motion of matter (through what is now time) that gives the impression of time distortion.

Remember what I said about pre-time force. It represents the whole energy of the universe moving around the creation event, slower toward the center and faster at the periphery. Creation is a steady state "explosion" out of which original creation came and still comes as the universe is sustained by a constant flow of that energy over mass as time.

Consider the example of a bicycle wheel where the spokes converging at the center move more slowly than they do where the rubber meets the road. At any point along any spoke, the motion there is mathematically constant, slower or faster, and predictable in relation to its distance from the center.

The motion of pre-time, at that special far-flung clotting "distance" from the center, must have sufficient motion or velocity to spin itself into matter and keep creation from dissolving back into timewind (or pre-time force, time motion if you will).

WHY TIME MUST BE A STEADY STATE

What if it were possible to travel toward the universal hub (of course, it isn't) where the pre-time force slows down? At that point, matter would start to come unraveled, not having sufficient motion to keep spinning, and would then dissolve back into pre-time force—becoming "no thing" as we know it.

I have also said that were it possible to ride with the motion of pre-time exactly, time as we know it would also cease, and hypothetically any existing matter would fuse with pre-time. (Of course, matter cannot "catch up" to nonexistence.) But the remarkable point I am trying to make is that here is a motion that actually exists without the need for time, and this "timeless motion" comes from the hub, the absolute, inertial, true timelessness from which all things have sprung.

THE MORAL:
WHERE THE END IS, THERE ALSO IS THE BEGINNING

What a simple and magnificent thing of endless beauty is time. Time is so simple that it is complicated. The human mind can hardly grasp it. The truth has always been difficult for egos in denial; somehow, we tend to make things more difficult, if only for that sense of achievement that would otherwise be denied us if things were easy to see, to grasp, and to achieve.

God's truth and His pathway are always in plain sight, however much our egos complicate them. Higher revelation with its clearer sight would compel us to serve a nobler purpose than our own. Sadly, we are usually too self-serving to see the obvious, in this case the unfolding of creation in a natural effortless way. We need only to be an unbiased witness to its marvelous unfolding.

It isn't that we can't understand what God has in store for us;

it is that we won't. The ego mind, confronted with such reality, shuts down—threatened by the presence of the Creator God who is greater than us all. There is something about our pride-driven intellect that wants no higher authority than itself.

Sensing the futility of the world as he knows it, man longs for the Ultimate Dimension. The interior of man needs to be formed by the everpresence of God's spirit. Man is essentially a spiritual being in corporeal form, potentially subject to God's Will and purpose. Outside that Will there are no centered men of Presence. Man is essentially lost, subject to time present, rather than to the Timeless Presence; thus man is torn farther and farther away from his true identity along with the expanding universe. What is missing in him is the understanding of what is happening to him, this dynamic of his free fall away from his Creator, as he is swept along by the gravity of creation. What man needs now is his soul's return to the inner realm of the timeless dimension, by way of atonement and a renewed faith in Him.

As you grow older, if time seems to speed up, it is only because you are spiritually slowing down and coming closer to your center. No longer lost in time's limiting flow, you are beginning to know what it is like to exist in a timeless realm, sitting on the bank of the river of life, outside creation, outside space/time, watching all the swimmers struggling against the current; now here you are at peace with God and nature, being in the world but no longer of it.

Five

GOD SCIENCE

"I was the hidden Treasure
I wanted to be known
Therefore I created the world
So that I would be known"

Sacred Sayings in Islam

We have established that the pre-time force "radial arms," circumorbiting from the timeless creation center, are in reality a form of motion without the need for time (as we experience it). I acknowledge that this is a bit difficult for us mortals to grasp, but please bear with me. We here on earth experience time because those pre-time "arms" continue to "blow" over us and pass us by, leaving us dragging in their "wind," a process which then converts that "wind" into time relative to our experience. Conversely, we have learned that time and space begin to disappear in direct proportion to any movement in the direction of this time "wind." In other words, steady state acceleration approaching the speed of light would tend to close the time/space gap at the approaches to these pre-time arms.

It is an established scientific fact that the faster we move, the slower a clock (traveling with us) ticks, and at some point as we approach light velocity—and perhaps beyond light velocity—time stops, and time/space disappears. Unfortunately for any space traveler, at that point, everything would be flattened, including the space traveler himself, by what would appear to be a dead stop—yet, amazingly, still moving.

Imagine the paradox of moving as fast as or faster than light and yet being totally stopped at the same instant. How would matter be squashed flat? There simply wouldn't be any space/time for matter to exist. Not only would your watch slow down and stop, there wouldn't be a watch at all, because there wouldn't be any space for it. There would be no time, no space, and no distance. And yet, whatever might be left would still be moving—moving and still at the same instant. We might even question whether there would be anything at all left moving—more likely there would be just pure motion—or to be more accurate, pre-time force, an other-dimensional, timeless motion. This is, of course, a pure thought experiment. None of this is practically possible since mass would gather energy into itself, becoming impossibly heavy.

No flesh and blood, nothing made of matter, can step across that border and still exist. But just beyond that point, there is another dimension—a parallel universe. The Bible has always maintained that flesh and blood cannot enter the Kingdom of God.

Remember what I said about those pre-time arms that swirl out of the timeless creation event: that they were/are motion—pre-time motion, force, energy. Think of them as motion that does not require time. Think of them as motion from which time and creation (as we know them) came—popping, as it were, out of that inter-dimensional "nothing." What do I mean by nothing? Well, it is not so much a "nothing" as a "no thing," yet-to-be things. This prephysical energy motion is a "no thing" as long as it has not assumed mass form and function in space/time. The pre-time motion arms are like that glowing radar screen, sweeping around and around, leaving blips of matter on the screen of creation. Such blips simulate the "spinning out" of matter, left behind by those pre-time arms, scanned and re-illuminated with every "radar" sweep. With each pass of the pre-time arm, atoms are "spun" and thus all matter is sustained in time and in circumorbital existence.

Note: Of course, the radar-like sweep mentioned herein is three-dimensional, but for the sake of clarity, I have again used a two-dimensional explanation of this pre-time force phenomenon—the "radar" model.

"Distance in time and space" is simply the difference between where the glowing radar arm in our two-dimensional model is still "moving," and where the "blip" of matter "popped" into existence is left behind in what becomes the time wind.

Were it possible (it isn't) for that blip of primordial matter to be reunited with the motion of the "radial arm" which is connected to the Still Center, the space between the blip and the arm would disappear and take the blip with it. They would merge. (Of course, this is absolutely impossible, but it makes the point.) However, theoretically speaking, if it were possible, the "matter blip" would conceivably once again fuse and become part of the whole arm, which is still and moving at the same time as a pre-creation phenomenon, centered in the creative event.

If it were possible to live on that moving arm (the pre-time force) where no time and space can exist (you would have to be a spiritual being to do this), you would be able to move in a dimension where there is no time, and no space as we know it. Here is a kind of eternity, a timeless quickening which is almost impossible for us mere mortals to realize. The leading edge of pre-time force defines the boundary whence the physical world came, where the spiritual eternal meets the physical infinite.

A "STILLNESS" MOVING FASTER THAN LIGHT

Imagine yourself standing at the center of a circle. Now look at any point on the perimeter and fix your attention there, drawing a clear line of sight. If that circle were a wheel and that fixed line of sight a spoke in that wheel, no matter how fast that circle were to turn with you at the hub, nothing would appear to be moving as long as you kept your eye fixed on that point, and there was no relevant background.

Along your line of sight nothing moves; your stillness extends out of the center, but of course it is a "moving stillness." This describes the behavior of that pre-time force I spoke of earlier, emanating from a still center. Remember that in the context of creation, this moving stillness eventually becomes time and space to us. If you could be with God and stand at the center of the universe right now, you would be at the source of the creation event—the absolute inertial stillness. The center does not know time as we do for "to God a thousand years are but a day. Nay, not even a day."

If you could look at a fixed point on the horizon of the universe as it revolved about you, you would not see or experience motion. However, let's say that you started to move along that line of sight. You still wouldn't experience motion. Everything would be perfectly still to you. Now consider walking out on that metaphoric line to the edge of the universe. Even as you moved out, you would experience no motion (except that of your own moving). You would not experience any motion like the motion we experience here in this created universe. Bear with me; this is a mystery we are talking about. What I am trying to say is that it is possible to move in a spiritual dimension without time—in other words, in a pre-time dimension.

Let me emphasize that within the boundary of the known universe, coexisting with us is this other dimension into which we cannot enter, unless we are spiritual beings who, of course, can exist in both places. For spirit can enter into matter, but matter cannot enter into spirit.

That the spirit can enter into matter is witnessed by the soul of man, and the Spirit of God who quickens it. And the door to this spiritual dimension lies within our grasp just beyond the stillness of our souls. And there it waits across the border of our flesh where only the noble and perfected souls can travel. Here we can live forever moving and having our being in a timeless way.

Part of you now, even as you read, bears witness to what I say here. Alas, this part is also being tugged in another direction, pulled down by the gravity of creation, the slavish obedience of our souls to the conditioning of sin. You may measure how far you are from the eternal life by becoming aware of the "gravity pull" of your slavish reactions, your oversensitivity to stress, which represents your slavery to sin. The prideful soul does not have an affinity or yearning for God. It is not obedient to Him. Together with its own "flesh," it is attached to the love of the world—an affection for the creature rather than the Creator. It is thus doomed to remain in this dimension of time and space, fully identified with the body's demise, and the final dissolution beyond.

Everywhere from the center to the curved horizon of the universe, this pre-time/timeless motion encompasses us. Imprisoned in our matter form we have an existence limited by time. We need to use this time wisely to find our timeless end at the beginning. The entrance to this parallel universe, this Kingdom of Heaven, is within us all; it is the Alpha and Omega referred to in scripture. In the *Gospel of Thomas*, the disciples asked Jesus, "Tell us how our end will be." Jesus said, "Have you discovered, then, the beginning, that you look for the end? For where the beginning is, there will be the end. Blessed is he who will take his place in the beginning; he will know the end and will not experience death."

THE MAGIC OF SLOWING DOWN

Sitting in an armchair is about as slow as anyone can go in this life, and yet in the macrocosm, we are not only moving, but we are moving at tremendous velocity through space. Without meditation seeking this stillness, we cannot slow down simply because any physical attempt toward slowness in any direction can only be a greater motion in the direction of timeless annihilation.

Only the repentant soul who has used this time on earth to shed the gravitational pull of sin is free to step across the inner void to eternal life.

Somewhere beyond the velocity of light there exists this leading edge of eternity. Somewhere beyond the swirling pre-time arms of timeless motion is the parallel dimension, a universe in which spiritual beings move and have their eternal being, the center of which is the Light of God—the Light of creation, the Light of souls—the everpresent Shedder of eternal light upon the cosmos. God is omnipresent. He transcends the time/space continuum. He operates independently of the dimensions of length, height, width, and time.

Here in the everlasting Now, souls are eternally renewed in the light of the Eternal Son. Remember though, while this dimension—the universe and its inhabitants—came from a physical beginning through time and space, the way back to our Spiritual Beginner is within—full circle.

Those who find the stillness of their spirit are born of this light, and remolded through their minds from within. While their outer earthly bodies were in motion, their inner souls were being formed, shaped from this still, timeless realm; so at the dissolution of their earthly form, they step across to the other side, compatible with the light from which they were formed.

And one day those reborn of God shall return to this earth, reclothed in a new kind of covering—and for them, there will be no second death. For the final resting place of man is this earth, this emerald isle. And the home of God is man made in His image. "Know ye not that ye are the temple of the Living God, and the Spirit dwelleth within?"

Six

COMPLEX MATTER FROM SIMPLE ENERGY

"At the beginning God expressed Himself. That personal expression, that Word, was with God and was God, and He existed with God from the beginning. All creation took place through Him, and none took place without Him. In Him appeared life, and this life was the light of mankind. The light still shines in the darkness, and the darkness has never put it out."

St. John 1:1 Phillips Translation

It is unlikely that any electron microscope will ever see the particle I call the origitron, the smallest in the universe. The origitron is so infinitely tiny that it could conceivably pass through all the subatomic spaces of which matter is mostly comprised, shining through the entire earth like a ray of light through a pane of glass.

One can only assume that the origitron exists because it is so tiny as to be virtually undetectable; in fact, it is so tiny, it practically doesn't exist at all—you might say it is on the borderline of existence. If that is true, and if we build on that "cause and effect" thesis, we should eventually arrive (going from logical assumption to logical assumption) at an identifiable aspect of the origitron's nature.

When these tiny particles are pushed through linear space, they radiate what could be called drag waves (or bow waves).

I have tried to show how origitrons, which are primal matter, actually dropped out of the pre-time force. As this primal matter came into existence, space/time also appeared in the very same instant. In other words, space/time came forth as an immediate expression, an extension, of primal matter. All came forth in such quick succession that one could hardly separate the parts of the process. In this sense, it is not hard to grasp the Biblical description of creation when God said "Let there be," and there was. For there is no space without time, no time without matter, no matter without primal pre-time force, and no pre-time force without God.

THE CREATION OF COMPLEX MATTER

Let's follow the logic of creation and examine how in a twinkling of an eye more complex structures must have been built from these tiny origitron building blocks.

Imagine the path of just two origitrons, made up of what I liken to "frozen" pre-time energy, spinning circumorbitally, having "clotted" out of pre-time force. Think of the origitrons as little chunks of ice in a river. Next visualize what these two particles experience as a result of their birth into matter as they drag in what now, because of their mass, has become a time current for them.

Visualize that time river pushing these origitrons along in a strong current moving at billions of times the speed of light. And this violent pre-time current is moving these little "chunks" of its own "frozen" self along, creating a "bow wave" effect at the "stern" where the origitrons drag in the "river" current flowing by and pushing them along. (When I say "stern wave" I am just using a two-dimensional model for simplicity's sake.) Notice also how those little solidified particles cannot keep up with the incredible force of the time river. The effect is that of a reverse bow wave (from the stern), a drag wave which is created as the river rushes past the particles.

The reason I use ice as an example is that ice is an allotrope of water, even as a diamond is an allotrope of carbon, meaning it is exactly the same chemistry but in a different form. I use ice to illustrate that matter is simply pressurized, "crystallized" pre-time force flowing now in what has become to it a river of time. Although the analogy is imperfect, imagine again if you will that the "time river" is pushing these little "chunks of its solidified self" along, creating the effect of a stern wave.

By this theory, I claim that light does not move under its own power, but is being pushed by pre-time force. In fact, all matter in the universe moves with a basic motion because of the presence of this mysterious background force. Humans made of heavier mass, moving with the earth, move much more slowly than light which passes us by as though we were standing still. In other words, mass moves slower than light and light moves slower than pre-time force, but everything is in relative motion to the Absolute Rest.

Since matter itself is made up of many subatomic particles, we must consider how these larger particles may have developed from the tiny origitron. How could such little particles of energy come together to create newer and more complex forms? The essential ingredient in this continued birthing process is still the tremendous pressure (perhaps super pulsations) of pre-time force.

I cannot comprehend creation as happening without the employment of some unusual force, since much more pressure than ordinary light velocity is needed to bring these particles together. We know that light meeting light does not create matter. Remember, primitive particles are still small enough to be affected by the great pressure of pre-time force. As matter evolves into grosser forms, it becomes less subject to this primary pressure force, and thus requires a different building process to continue its evolution. Let us first consider the earliest forms of matter creation which require super acceleration.

SUPER PRIMAL VELOCITY

At the creation event level, subatomic particles were (and still are) pushed along by pre-time force much faster than light velocity, therefore creating: A) much bigger drag waves than usual, and B) primitive gravity. Hold these two thoughts in mind as I proceed with my explanation.

For the sake of discussion, let us pretend for a moment that just two origitron particles are now boats or vessels passing each other in the ocean. Observe the effect of their ripples or bow waves and how the two ships affect one another in their passing. Relate this to how these two origitrons might interact with each other in coming together to form a larger particle, one with entirely new properties of matter.

Now let's take a closer look at what origitrons really are and how they interact. Of course, they are not solid like a boat. As primal force/matter, they are more like spinning whirlpools, which, by the nature of their spinning, possess what we might call weight (resistance to motion). Clearly, their spinning makes them "heavier" than the relatively linear force that created them. Following this logic, because the whirlpool-like origitrons have "weight," they drag in the pre-time force, and just like any object floating in a river they cause drag waves. Thus, we have a whirlpool wave and, because of its drag, we have a wave around the whirlpool. In this context, the first wave is primitive mass, and the second wave is caused by the motion of the mass. The whirlpool waves that have become mass produce waves that are not mass. In other words, one kind of wave creates another kind of wave. The first is the basis of what we call a solid and the second is the root of an energy field that becomes gravitational, magnetic, and electric in that order.

Two whirlpool-like origitrons approaching each other at greater than light speed from any direction disturb the space/time medium in such a way as to draw the origitrons around (or into) each other. I am not specifying whether these two elementary forms actually blend together or simply circum-orbit each other perpetually; the key is only that they come together and form something greater than themselves. Of course, it is mere speculation as to which occurs. Perhaps at different stages of matter development both occur—first one and then the other—first forming larger whirlpools and then for some dynamic reason, whirlpools orbiting whirlpools and so on.

There is a logic to this that is fun to consider: There must be a minimum whirlpool able to maintain itself, forming the smallest particle of energy, the origitron. Likewise, there must be a maximum whirlpool particle that cannot maintain itself in any larger state, but can hold other "weights" in orbit. The next stage of formation depends on orbital relationships of these whirlpool creations.

Two Forms of Gravity

In considering the smallness of a particle, we have to include the concept of gravity. Otherwise, what holds things together? At this juncture, let me say there are two forms of gravity: one caused by a steady state acceleration, which Einstein said is indistinguishable from gravity. I believe that this form of gravity mostly concerns the primitive stages of the creation of matter, caused by the sheer "steady state" pressure of massive acceleration of the primal winds. The other form of gravity which we will discuss later concerns the presence of huge masses in space which by their nature warp space/time. This form of gravity does not depend on acceleration, but only on its massive presence in space/time.

Of course, all mass by its nature possesses gravity. Subatomic particles in their creation formation, themselves, have gravity by virtue of their inward spin, maintained by the pressure applied to them by the pre-time force which is time to them.

Larger mass has a different gravity because, as Einstein stated, the mass distorts the space/time medium around it. This, I say, causes a pressure or a push on all surfaces of larger mass that is called gravity. The beauty of all this is that both forms, the particle and gross mass, have gravity due to their relationship with the unifying pre-time space/time field—one by virtue of its motion through space/time and the other due to its massive presence in space/time. Einstein was right when he said that steady state acceleration is indistinguishable from gravity. However, more than that, steady state acceleration and gravity are not merely indistinguishable; they are the same—simply different manifestations of the same origin.

While Einstein said that the steady state of acceleration was indistinguishable from gravity, it is not sustainable gravity as it applies to already created mass. Where steady state acceleration gravity does apply is in the creation of essential mass—the smallest particle I have called the origitron.

In his theories about steady state acceleration and the Equivalence Principle, Einstein was actually describing the force required for the creation of matter. This force takes on another form in post-creation reality which Einstein knew was a phenomenon equivalent to steady state acceleration—real gravity as we know it.

Once primal matter (possibly "dark matter") is formed, steady state acceleration energy ceases to be a factor. Remember that the origitron is nothing more than steady state accelerated energy that has gravitationally compressed itself into mass. While steady state acceleration is a form of gravity, it is not the gravity of existing creation. Steady state acceleration simply brings creation to the point of existence.

I know that some of these chapters are more difficult to read than others, both scientifically and spiritually. If you found this chapter particularly hard to absorb, I hope you will give it a second reading. Doing so may help a great deal.

Seven

THE UNIVERSE
A MATHEMATICAL MIRACLE

*"Nature is an endless
combination and repetition
of a very few laws."*

Ralph Waldo Emerson

Consider the unique relationship between zero and one in mathematics and you have some idea of where I am going with this chapter. It is the zero that gives the one its meaning. For the purposes herein, think of the zero as "stillness" and the one as "first motion." This sets up a dynamic universal model of relative stillnesses and motions out of which the universe is made.

The "one" of pre-time force—first motion—that gave birth to the universe is, even now (and forever), swirling around us, coming from every direction in space/time. It is a pre-dimensional "moving stillness" acting upon its creation in myriad ways. You might say the whole of this universe is bathed in another dimension. And yet, as I have said, this pre-time force gets its power from the "zero," the still creation center, the hub of the force that makes it all possible.

Just as the zero is the hub of numbers, negative numbers to one side and positive to the other, the universe is an explosion of center-focused geometries. Planetary relationships are one obvious example, but consider the microcosm. In the atom, the bulk of the energy is not represented by the orbiting electrons, but is locked up in the center—the nucleus. So likewise is the mighty power of the entire turning universe not represented by the orbiting of all creation, which is seen, but by the metaphysical nucleus that remains unseen. The power of creation lies not in the physical universe, but is hidden in that abstract dimension, in the absolute calm, metaphysical center. Here resides the Everpresent Being, the Prime Mover of all that moves, the One who remains Himself unmoved. Absolute rest is possible without absolute motion—but absolute motion cannot exist without absolute rest.

FIRST MOTION

Pre-time force, the first motion, is the essence of creation. It is the power emerging from, and in relationship to, the still "eye of the storm." This everpresent moving "stillness" is a force the velocity of which could be described as millions of times faster than the speed of light—of course, what I mean is that it's a figure so far beyond comprehension that it makes measurement meaningless. We recognize it as time, and I believe that this pre-time (time) force is a power waiting to be tapped and harnessed by mankind in the next century. It is great enough to create mass, and great enough to maintain the motion of the galaxies. It is a force beyond our knowing but scientifically still within our grasp because we experience it in this dimension as time/gravity.

The making of mass required enormous pressures at the "periphery" of creation, allowing cosmic matter to spring into existence in an "explosive" event. An originating force, many times more powerful at the center than the entire energy/mass of the present cosmos, God's willed action came spinning out of the cosmic center. It compelled pre-time force to spin around making itself into "heavy" little fireballs of motion—origitrons—which, once created, dragged in the wake of the force that made them. This pre-time force then became time as we know it, instantly taking the measure of all creation.

FIELD EFFECTS AND AURAS

Everything in the universe is made up of origitrons, the basic building blocks. They are the substance of the atom's nucleus as well as of its orbiting electrons. The electrons in each atom, depending on the element, are of a particular number, as are the particles that make up the nucleus. Thus elements are pure mathematics, increasing in mass as the numbers within the nucleus increase. Each atomic number yields a different chemistry, and hence a different field effect. Atoms combine with one another to become molecules, complex structures producing an endlessly expanding variety of field effects—everything from stars and planets to animals and flowers have their own signature effect. The field effect around anything, based on its geometries, makes it what it is, and that effect is what the Creator had in mind from the very beginning.

The role played by geometry in describing the physical properties of all matter and life forms is the miracle of creation. The cosmos is a geometric variation of spinning, gyrating fireballs, and the field (the peculiar effect immediate to itself) around the infinite configurations of gyrating particles is the cause-and-effect phenomenon of matter. A "field" is the effect that every creation has on its immediate environment—such as the magnetic, electric and gravitational field.

Try to imagine the field effect around a truly whole, God-centered being. The energy flowing through and around him would be other-dimensional, possessing a quality, a reality, unlike that of any other created being in the universe. When the creature truly experiences the Creator, creation becomes subject to him rather than dominating him, thus reversing man's former slavish struggle with his environment, ultimately even giving him dominion over time, and over his own mortality. Whenever such "creation force" (God's presence) touches a mortal soul, the soul becomes saved, transformed and renewed. A new spiritual being emerges, remolded through his mind from within, reflecting the person and the character of the Creator/Savior. God intended man to be the crowning glory of His creation.

EVOLUTION OF VELOCITY/MOMENTUM

Everything is transforming everything, and everything is becoming everything else. From the beginning, from the "no thing" comes the "some thing" which becomes all things.

Mass is energy and energy possesses mass. However, if we apply different momentums, pressures, or forces to little particles, then forces acting on those particles cause different behaviors or evolve into more complex forms of matter with unique field behaviors. Swirls of energy become whirlpools, which become greater whirlpools, eventually orbiting other energy whirlpools. Simplicity of motion becomes complexity of matter.

Through time, the evolution of momentum keeps transforming the basic geometry into different sizes, shapes, forms, functions, combinations, compounds, and behaviors, each represented by a center or nucleus. Everything has a center of its wholeness that is the cause of its full effect, which effect, in turn, becomes a central cause for another wholeness, the effect standing upon it. In other words, the Original (motion and rest) Principle keeps transforming into different shapes, forms, effects, and behaviors—making up the whole of creation.

Allow me to emphasize the main points once more: Pre-time force velocity becomes matter and then goes on to become space/time/gravity with respect to matter. Like those glowing blips on the radar screen that brighten with each sweep of the "radar arm," so also is all creation for-

ever sustained, its matter whipped like spinning tops
by pre-time winds.

If time were to stop flowing, all matter would cease to exist in
the twinkling of an eye, and in that same twinkling of an eye the
whole universe would vanish. The spinning action of mass is
not a perpetual motion, but one defined and maintained by the
constant velocity/momentum of the primordial energy that I
call pre-time force.

The Incomprehensible Power of Creation

The velocity required to push pre-time force out and whip it
into matter is enormous, beyond human comprehension. Once it
is compressed into matter, this energy slows down and is regulated internally at the speed of light. The fact that this energy circumorbits "itself" is what makes energy appear solid. The gyroscopic effect of spinning, circumorbiting energy that we call
mass causes the resistance to motion and gives matter its relative
inertial stability. A similar effect can be experienced when one
tries to move a spinning gyroscope. It will feel heavy to the touch
and it will resist being pushed over. In other words, it gains a kind
of pseudo-weight, thanks to its spinning.

At the time of this writing, physicists have succeeded in using
a particle accelerator to drive two smaller particles together to
make a bigger one. The effect has been described as being like
that of two tennis balls crashing together and throwing out a larger bowling ball. Much of the energy needed to push those "tennis
ball" particles at sufficient velocity becomes incorporated into
the larger "bowling ball" particle. In other words, some of the
energy needed to drive the "fireballs" together assumes "mass,"
and incorporates itself into the two particles, producing a particle
larger than the sum of its two parts.

Once you consider the gigantic human effort required to produce this one little particle, perhaps then you can see the marvel of perpetually creating matter out of "nothing" and accelerating smaller particles into bigger ones—all on the scale of the size of the universe. While it is obviously possible to grow larger particles from smaller ones, we need to appreciate also how much intelligence is at work behind all the phenomena of creation.

The smaller particles in question, which scientists snowballed into a larger particle, had to be accelerated to a velocity whereby those gravity "bow waves" discussed earlier appeared around the respective particles. Whereas any two massive bodies attract one another in space by virtue of their actual gravity, subatomic particles combine and interlock by way of the gravity (space/time distortion) generated around their mutual velocities, thus incorporating their respective energies into one larger form.

This explanation leads to an obvious question: Why doesn't light from distant stars, traveling through space, become matter? The answer is that light doesn't travel fast enough. Ordinarily, light velocity is limited by the opposing timewind. What light would need in order to transform into mass is the awesome velocity of the creation event, clotting and clumping itself into matter at the horizon of the creation event. Those who doubt the spectacular transformation that pressure can produce need only look at a diamond: black carbon in the form of graphite, a soft lubricant, can under pressure become diamond-hard and clear as crystal—with no new elements added. It seems like a miracle, but the process is straightforward enough; the same element, transformed by pressure, yields totally new properties. Thus pre-time force velocity under its own pressure becomes space/time/gravity/mass; it is creation formed from the very beginning, transformed by pressure alone, just like the diamond.

Now that you have some idea of how much energy is required to grow matter from smaller particles, try to imagine how much more energy it would take to push gross matter, like a rocket ship, toward light speed. The following are some hypothetical speculations on what could happen if you possessed enough energy to do the job: First, it would take all the power in the universe to push that rocket to velocities of light against the time wind resistance that regulates the motion of matter at much lower speeds than that of light. So if you did possess all the power necessary, the amount required to do the pushing might well incorporate itself into the rocket ship, snowballing it into a larger mass, needing even more energy. The energy again would add to the mass of the ship, slowing it and making it heavier—thus demanding even *more* energy, which then becomes its own matter in an evolving, self-defeating process going nowhere. In other words, the faster you go, the heavier you are; the heavier you are, the more energy it takes to push you—and the heavier still you become. Remember, a planet is not one ball, but a system of innumerable tiny spinning arrangements of subatomic matter we call atoms and molecules. This describes the problems inherent in using steady state acceleration gravity, a force that I believe created original matter, to evolve more complex matter forms.

Laws of nature permitting, there might be a second possibility: Let's pretend that the rocket ship could be brought to light speed without becoming an impossibly heavy blob. You would still encounter serious problems. For one thing, our astronaut along with his ship would be crushed as flat as a pancake against the pressure of the time wind resistance as space/time compressed and ceased to exist. Gross matter simply cannot attain light velocity. Timewind imposes its speed limits on all its creations and, thus, all matter acts uniquely with respect to the law established by the existence of the pre-time/wind force.

Now stretch your imagination to even greater lengths of implausibility. There is a third reason why gross matter could not survive light speed. Suppose you were able to push that rocket ship beyond light speed, and you actually caught up to the pre-time force arm, touching it. The rocket ship, astronaut and all, might then fuse into the timeless pre-time "arm" and cease to exist as mass, because they would have passed out of existence into the spiritual realm where matter cannot go—at least not with any worldly pushing. For beyond that border lies the other dimension, the Kingdom of Heaven that can be entered only through the inner door of our soul.

IF SPACE IS A VOID, WHY THE RESISTANCE?

It is a well known precept in mechanical physics that in space there is no resistance to material bodies—no friction, such as there is, for example, in a medium like air. Thus it is believed that a moving mass will remain in motion forever. As a result, science has concluded that since space does not disturb matter in motion, there can be no interaction between matter and space.

Here I believe we have overlooked something important. Just because there is no resistance to matter that we can measure doesn't mean there is no resistance at all. After all, we know that matter cannot be pushed as fast as light; so it would seem that there must be some degree of resistance. Why is it that matter cannot reach light speed? And why is it that light itself is limited? What is doing the resisting?

The answer lies in the Creator's wisdom in setting a lower speed limit for matter than for subatomic particles such as light. You would not want to find yourself in a universe that has only one speed limit. You need a hierarchy of limits (with various arrangements of motion and rest) for the universe to work, a geometry of motions to give the order of elements to creation. If the universe had only one limit, then somewhere above light velocity (where I believe energy is converted into mass) universal energy would simply snowball. There would be no defining motions, functions, and chemistries, and if this process were to be endlessly extended, the result would be one huge, universal "growth" filling the universe in a meaningless, non-creative way. There would be no evolution beyond that one giant amorphous blob of single, elemental, energy-absorbing, unstable sameness. There would be no succession of laws governing cause and effect, and allowing matter to have the infinite variety of symmetries we call creation—compartmentalized, dynamic systems, governed independently, allowing creation within creation within creation.

Thankfully, the pre-time/time force I have described not only provides the "friction" necessary to create limits and cause regulation, but it also provides the universal energy. In fact, this energy of creation (blowing and swirling around us) might actually be available and useful to us if we could tap into it and control it. If this proves to be true, let us hope mankind has the spiritual maturity to handle it.

THE ETERNAL MAN—THE LIVING END

In the order of creation, the same force (pre-time) which is the friction of time to the created world, now causes a friction within us all. As it comes flowing up from within us as time-less love, we are given a chance to seek beyond the world we know. Where the end of our spiritual journey is, there is also for us a new beginning. We are to be the ultimate temple of God. Whereas God created the universe through time from the beginning—from the beginning also He entered the world by way of His most beloved expression—His only begotten Son who gave the world a new breed of man.

From the wellspring of the Father comes the eternal gift; He who gives us the life of time now also offers us the timeless life. How can this be grasped? God is uniquely able to commune with mankind through the interior of our being. Time is clear and tangible evidence of its own timeless root. Time is to the material creation what timelessness is to the spiritual. Like the iceberg protruding above the surface of the ocean, time is extending out and flowing through the timeless realm into creation. The timeless realm is the sinless, perfect parallel universe.

All of us can share in this timeless universal characteristic, which already lies within us, waiting to unfold. For we have a hand within a hand, a foot within a foot; we see as well as perceive; we hear as well as understand. We choose hands of good or evil and things occur. With feet, we walk in the way that makes us subjects of the world or sons and daughters of the Kingdom of God within.

No Excuses

The universe is more than pure science; it is an awesome, overwhelming mathematical miracle—nothing becomes something—motion becomes matter. And yet, we are told that this marvel is only a glimpse of what is to come. "The eye has not seen, nor the ear heard, neither has it entered into the heart of man what God has prepared for those that love Him." Everywhere in physics is the evidence of Love. However, our pride resists confronting a greater Truth than our own, a greater Love than human love. When we mortals play God by living in and through our imaginations, we construct realities of our own, and science of our own. It is His Science we must seek, both of the cosmos and of the heart. Nothing else works.

God's imaginings are not vain like ours—His Will is real. The universe is made not without scientific basis (since He created science). The process of creation has within it an underlying scientific order and sustaining principles all the way back to the pre-science beginning in the heart/mind of God. For although He created from a place we cannot see or understand, His Creation itself is understandable. We have no excuse.

MIRACLES

So we've gone full circle once again, from the evolution of time/matter/space right up to the completion of man in God's image, the commingling of both worlds. The spiritual becomes the material and the spiritual enters into the material through each of us. Truly where the end is, there also is the beginning, full circle. They are one and the same "place."

God prepared a place on earth for man, His creature with whom He desires to identify. For His spiritual dimension is not creation; it just is. The universe, on the other hand, is an artistic, architectural marvel, created from the "no thing" of His Spirit which brings the spiritual into this dimension by way of man.

When God creates, He does not create for amusement. He creates because God is Love and needs to create, and love other than Himself. Therefore He has created the creature to acknowledge its Creator through the wonders of His creation. Standing in humility and in awe of God's creation (a form of worship), man can receive the Creator's Love, and this genuine Love is the only kind that man can give or have for God. However, the ego of man can choose to reject that Love, wanting instead to be the object of human love, an unreliable source. Little wonder that the world is so full of tragedy and suffering.

Christ transcended the fall of man, bringing a new light into the world, transcending chaos, overshadowing death, bearing perfect witness to God's redeeming Grace, bringing to believers in this dimension the completion of the work of His Father.

Christ didn't need to split the atom for the miracle of the loaves and fishes. Nor did Moses need to harness nuclear forces to divide the Red Sea. The energy for these marvels existed all around them as it does to this very day. That energy is the timewind essence, out of which anything can be made to appear and disappear in the twinkling of an eye. Nothing is impossible with God.

A soul in harmony with its Creator Cause, such as that of Abraham, Moses, or Paul, shares in the Word, the Willed Action of God's Purpose. We too can be conduits of His Will from the spiritual into this material dimension, fully capable of transmitting God's purpose on earth as it is in Heaven. We need no gurus or priests on this earth to intercede for us, although they are as inevitable as political leaders.

In whatever field you can name, some authorities have good intent, others do not. Even now, as you read these words, some physicists egocentrically seek to exploit the secrets of the smallest subatomic particles. This kind of scientist knows intellectually that the closer he gets to this source of power, the more he can hope to play God by reassembling divine marvels from his own human will and intelligence. The pure miracle of God's Science is hidden from him by his own ego and ambition.

Ironically, the power we attempt to grasp could be ours for the asking. A God-like man has the power (if he is so willed by the Creator) to instantly organize and pull together the time energy in which we are all bathed and thereby to produce any effect desired—what we call miracles (and of course they are). However, spiritual miracles are not the subject of this writing. The miracle we must appreciate first is how the universe was created, and how it is still being created (energized) out of "nothing."

It is essential for the created to realize that God is the Creator, and to live in awe and wonder of that fact. If you fail to know Him by His creation, then you cannot know him as the Creator and receive the vital force of His love. Worship Him now so that one day nothing will be impossible to you.

Eight

PRIMAL STILLNESS AND ANTIGRAVITY

*"Our whole business in this life is
to restore health to the eye of the
heart, whereby God may be seen."*

St. Augustine

In this chapter, we are trying to come to terms with the border between the physical dimension and its other-dimensional, spiritual beginning. This requires a little groundwork, so please bear with me.

As I have stated and restated, motion is defined by what is still. The universe is in motion, circumorbiting the absolute inertial stillness of the creation event. And yet, since space/time motion does not apply there, this God-center Stillness cannot be the standard that defines the motion of the physical dimension.

Therefore, there must exist in the physical dimension a primal standard relative stillness, one by which all the motions in the universe—rippling beyond that benchmark stillness—might be "measured and regulated," including the velocity of light itself.

If the velocity of light is a constant, then what makes it so? What are the regulating forces, and by what standard of "stillness" is the velocity of light measured? If the motion of mass is limited to a speed less than light velocity, where is the reference point by which mass "knows" it is approaching its speed limit? By what (relative) standard is "faster" or "slower" measured? Where is the starting gate, the law by which the motions of both light and matter are policed and regulated? The answer is primal stillness.

Let us say you are in your home, office, or perhaps the park. You are sitting quietly, perfectly still from your frame of reference.

However, as I have said previously, looking down on yourself from space, you would see your location rotating on a big ball we call Earth, not to mention its other motion around the sun.

Let's say you decide to go for a drive. Whichever direction you choose, north, east, south, or west, your still (but yet moving) location would be the starting point in your journey.

Now let's say you return home and are again sitting in your living room, and a big storm arises. No matter from which direction the wind blows, you would obviously measure the wind's velocity based on the coordinates of your "still" home. You would surely not take into account that your house is also rotating on the earth's axis, or that the earth itself revolves around the sun. As far as we Earthlings are concerned, wherever we are on the surface of this rotating planet, that spot is the "still" home base for measuring our movements. It is a moving, yet "still" home base, providing a criterion by which we measure everything that moves around us, including our own comings and goings. Similar coordinates must exist in the universe by which all velocities of light and matter are measured and regulated. If you lived on a planet revolving twice as fast as ours, surely 30 mph would be just 30 mph, and stillness would be just as still. However, your stillness would actually be twice as "fast" as our stillness. Thus, there are two different standards of stillness by which we would measure our respective speeds of 30 mph. It is all relative.

SO, WHAT ON EARTH IS STILL?

Suppose now we burrow under the house towards the center of the earth—surely that center would be another "still" place (more still than our house rotating with the surface). Yet here we sit on the crust of the earth about 4000 miles above that central point beneath us—both places (relatively) still, and yet moving.

Now let us shift to a third perspective, outer space. At what distance would a satellite have to be positioned to be in a "stationary" geosynchronous orbit so that when you look up above the roof of your house the satellite hovers there, always "still," fixed in one place, exactly matching the surface rotation of your home? If we find that spot, then we have three places that are relatively still: the center of the earth, the house, and the satellite—all in alignment with one another, all "still," and yet in motion. You see, relative stillness is all we observers have by which to measure the motion of anything. Wherever we stand is that "relative stillness" to us—there are countless relative stillnesses. The universe is constructed from motions and stillnesses, with all "stillnesses" in motion. In other words, clearly the whole of the universe is in motion. "Freeze frame" this point. I am coming back to it later.

Let us say for argument's sake that the velocity of our satellite must be 17,000 miles per hour in order to be in geosynchronous (stationary) orbit over our house at a distance of 22,000 miles. Again, this satellite, as far as we are concerned, is hovering perfectly still, exactly overhead. It is just as "still" as our house is and yet, at the same moment in time, from a different frame of reference, it is moving much faster. The same would be true from the perspective of the earth's center, a much "slower stillness" than at the surface. All three locations would be in line with each other—all relatively still, yet moving at different speeds. So we have three different motions appearing at rest as (relative) stillnesses.

Perhaps I should clarify what I mean by "geosynchronous." By using that term I am trying to make a point, using physics, to describe a relationship with pre-physical central creation event reality—that is to say, before all the dimensions of time, space and matter. How can anyone describe a relationship between a "something" and a central, metaphysical "no thing?" And yet that is exactly what I am trying to do. So forgive the "geosynchronous orbit" analogy if it is less than crystal clear. Let me explain further to help you better understand.

The satellite balanced in orbit has a minimum velocity and a minimum distance from its "brother stillness" on the earth's surface. It cannot move faster without moving out of orbit and it cannot move slower without falling back to earth. That place of geosynchronous balance is similar to the threshold of primal relative stillness, the pre-physical dimension, the first in a chain of relative stillnesses that together move, and that actually make up the cause and effect of creation.

LOCATING PRIMAL STILLNESS

A satellite in geosynchronous orbit, like all the preceding examples, describes movement in relation to a reference point of relative stillness. But how can one describe a motion as relative to absolutely zero motion? Relativity we can understand, but a place of absolute rest is almost impossible to grasp. Then again, so is infinity. This slowest space where matter can exist is not just a spot. It exists everywhere as a centrifugal circumorbiting field around the creation rest—a field out of which matter "drops" and "hangs."

As I said before, there must be a primal standard of relative stillness against which to measure and regulate the motions of the universe, including light itself. There is a real scientific need for that space of primal relative stillness in the cosmos as the first in a long chain of relative stillnesses.

Primal stillness could also be called primal movement. It is a universal, relative rest that moves at the slowest speed in which creation (matter) can exist, synchronized with the absolute rest of the creation event. Let me say it again. It is the slowest "space" where matter can exist with respect to the First Cause, the Ultimate Relative, Uncaused Absolute Rest.

This "first" in the order of relative stillnesses is to be compared only to the center of the creation event—the Absolute Rest that science does not recognize. It can only be conjectured logically based on observation of cause and effect leading to a beginning cause that is not the effect of any other cause. And that cause is pre-physical (or metaphysical). The standard of primal stillness is everywhere in the sustainable universe. If it were possible to cause an object to move slowly enough to become positioned in that space, it would then physically define the place of primal stillness by which all motion is regulated, definable, and measurable according to the laws of physics. This "space" is the starting gate of all relative motions and stillnesses, and thus must be considered a theoretical standard of measurement.

All mass in the universe is moving at least as fast as primal stillness. Were it possible for heavenly bodies to go slower than this physical border of creation, they would "dissolve" back into the creation event energy, disappearing, perhaps opening a "black hole" void which in turn might suck other physicalities into sub-existent speed.

Just as the gravitational "pull" on the satellite tends to pull it down while its velocity tends to fling it out (resulting in a geosynchronous orbit), so too is there a "geosynchronous" space/time around the central creation event where matter exists without slowing out of existence and disintegrating.

Of course, as I have described it, the constant flow of steady state pre-time force (which we experience as time) would prevent such an event, in theory, much like Einstein's Cosmological Constant. There can be no "falling back" or "gravitational collapse" of the universe simply because the gravitational "weight" of the universe is itself an expression of the "forward" out-flowing of pre-time force. In any event, matter cannot "fall back" as matter. It can only dissolve into its pre-physical form if it crosses the "motion border" at the edge of existence.

GRAVITATIONAL COLLAPSE?

There is no way that the universe is going to fall back in some gigantic gravitational collapse, because matter gets its form from the out-flinging described here. Therefore, matter cannot fall back to some pre-bang clump. In order to do that, matter would have to go slower than the speed it needs to exist, and it would instantly dissolve. This also cannot happen because the creation forces that "spoke it" into existence are ever-flowing. On a universal level, the only way for matter to slow down is for the energy that gave it form to slow down, for God to "withhold His hand" and cause the end of time. However, it may be possible for some local phenomenon like a black hole to interrupt the creation flow and so cause a disintegration of matter, space, and time.

To use a mundane example, a man standing still relative to the earth is similar to matter's primal stillness. Can the man go slower than standing still? The answer is obviously no—and yet he isn't really still. We know he is actually moving with the rotating earth. This is a kind of primal stillness. He can move faster in any direction and yet he cannot go slower than standing still. Neither can matter go slower than it does in its natural state of existence.

If you were living on one of those earth-orbiting satellites in geosynchronous orbit, you could put on a space suit and use that satellite as a home base to travel to and fro in any direction. You would measure your speed and distance from the "still" satellite base that defines your motion in space.

The cosmos has just such a ubiquitous space/time in motion around the creation event. Countless billion light years in dimension, it is invisible and unmarked.

Primal stillness, the slowest stillness in the universe, existing everywhere, is the space from which the velocity of light and matter are regulated precisely by the laws of physics. This space can be theoretically calculated as existing everywhere in the cosmos, and from there—which is everywhere—the velocity of light should be measured in honest time, because that is where true time exists without distortion of motion above primal stillness.

The entire universe is in motion, circumorbiting its center "axis." Everywhere matter and light exist they are regulated by the laws of motion relative to that ubiquitous "space" of primal stillness we have been talking about.

Logically, there is also a "black" area connected to the creation event where the many processes of creation move too slowly for anything to form. I am not alluding to such a "place," but to the space in the sustainable universe where matter comes into existence and is sustained by coordinate winds of pre-time force. That space is the primal (relative) stillness by which the movements of stars and planets are not only measurable, but are also governed by their relationship with that slowest rhythm of the universe (their synchronicity with the primal stillness, with its general movement of the universe in one direction). As I have said, your house is just like one of those spaces. Can you move any slower than simply standing in your living room? Of course not. You can only go faster (by simply taking a step in any direction).

Again, primal stillness exists in the space where the theoretical coordinates of the timewinds intersect in a grid-like fashion—which is everywhere in the universe. Remember, we are trying to describe the boundary between the physical dimension and the metaphysical dimension that originates the physical.

Even without a satellite hovering over your house to demonstrate it, we can mathematically calculate that there does exist such a geosynchronous space, the evidence of which is that you can hang a satellite there and it will hover over your house as if "motionless." In like manner, there are theoretically identifiable points everywhere in the universe surrounding the creation event, spaces moving synchronously with the eye of the creation event. Each of those ubiquitous spaces represents a place of balance, the slowest that any mass can move and yet remain material—thus establishing a standard for real time.

I want the reader to understand that this is the benchmark for all the motions of creation. Let me emphasize that matter cannot move any slower than this synchronous motion lest it fall back and dissolve into "no-thingness."

As I said, we need not worry about mass falling back to the center creation event, because the "centrifugal" force of the outward bound motion of creation, as a kind of antigravity, keeps it from falling back. This constant flow of energy describes a living universe that totally contradicts the first and second laws of creation as postulated in the thermodynamics theory of creation.

Remember what I said about timewinds coming from all directions at once, and in the absence of mass, passing through themselves. With mass present, however, the timewind applies equal pressure from all directions, precisely defining that space where mass hangs in its slowest motion, moving precisely with the turning of the creation event, far, far away in the center of the universe—similar to that satellite fixed "motionless" over your house. Such a space is, as I said, everywhere in the universe where timewinds meet and intersect, defined by the presence of all mass at any point in space. In other words, where mass is present, the coordinates of timewind govern what its motion is. While the velocity of any mass can increase and can slow, it can never go slower than the constant pace set where the timewinds cross and blow.

Nine

HONEST AND DISHONEST TIME

*"...time was born along
with things which exist."*

Clement of Alexandria (c. AD 150-220)

In the last chapter I stated that primal stillness is the first place away from the Creation Center, from where space/time coordinates move in a synchronous fashion with that First Cause Stillness. It is the first in the order of moving stillnesses outward bound into the material universe, with respect to all other relative stillnesses of the cosmos. Here is where we have "honest" length, height, width, and time, the basic ground for mathematical science. Although probably nothing in the universe actually moves that slowly, nevertheless such coordinates exist.

This space can be defined theoretically, and is everywhere in space/time, moving synchronously with the swirling eye of creation's First Cause Stillness. Because this stillness then is first in the order of all the relative "moving stillnesses," I gave it the name "primal stillness." From the ubiquitous primal stillness coordinates, the speeds of light and matter are regulated, and from here-there-everywhere all other motions may be measured perfectly in honest time. There, light will be found to be measured at the understood 186,000.272 miles per second. Light also measures the same in distorted time (meaning with respect to objects in motion greater than that of primal stillness). We will get to that soon enough.

Remember, wherever primal stillness is, there too is honest time, that slowest-moving space/time where matter placed there can survive as matter. So honest time exists only at the point of primal stillness, which happens to be everywhere in the grid-like, converging lines of space/time's circumorbital motion. Objects do move faster than primal stillness, but never slower.

Let me say it again: Since the universe is created out of primal motion, there is a minimum physical velocity at which matter is created and sustained, slower than which matter cannot exist. As mentioned earlier, the basic building block of matter, the origitron, is a circumorbiting swirl that derives its very form from the original motion itself. It is a "no thing" thing.

The speed of light should also be measured with respect to this slowest point in space/time, the primal stillness. However, it is not. It is currently defined at the same velocity by observers regardless of their various motions. The main reason for this uniform measurement of light is that whatever an observer's motion is, light velocity is measured there in slower seconds relative to primal stillness seconds. A second is actually faster at primal stillness and slower compared with objects moving faster than primal stillness. In other words, the faster one moves through time, the slower the seconds. Therefore the speed of light can always be measured as the same regardless of how fast the observer moves, because the faster light is measured in slower seconds. Light is not necessarily constant; it may move in slightly varying speeds, but it is always measured the same, because whenever it strikes an object, its speed is relative to the observer's slower seconds.

Einstein said that light was the only constant and that time varies with the motion of an observer, that is to say, time moving slower for one person and faster for another. If that is so, how does any observer measure the velocity of light?—by time? If light measures at 186,000.272 miles per second in the faster time for one observer and the same velocity for an observer moving in slower time, what are we saying about light? I think we must be saying that time and light are co-factors. In other words, time—

even though it moves slower for one person than another—is constant with respect to light. The speed of light is exactly the same for both observers moving in nonuniform motion with respect to one another.

Scientists seem to overlook the fact that their constant of light, supposedly the only one in the universe, is measured by time. Yet they say that time slows with faster motion—the very same slower time used to measure light as a constant. It would seem that if light measures the same in slower time, then time must also be constant simply because the speed of light is always expressed in terms of time.

So I am saying that the measurement of light is always by the standard of time, and if time is said to move slower, that must say something also about light, which is measured in terms of time. How can it be said that light alone is the constant? Surely time should be included in that perception.

TIME/LIGHT: THE RELATIVE CO-CONSTANTS

Remember what I have said before: Light has a different relationship with primal space/time than it does as it encounters matter in motion. In other words, a beam of light traveling through space will be moving relative to the primal stillness exactly at light velocity in honest time. However, when it encounters moving mass its relativity changes with respect to the time factor of the moving object (and to the energy spinning as mass).

It is well understood that the faster one travels through space/time, the slower a clock ticks off seconds. This motion, faster than primal stillness motion, is distorted time, the kind caused by motion itself. Honest time exists only where the ever-present, primal stillness space exists. Therefore, it could be said that light can actually move faster, but in slower seconds, with respect to objects moving faster than primal stillness. What I am saying is that light moves through space/time with respect to primal space as well as with respect to the motion of objects. In a sense, light could be said to have a double standard—moving at different velocities, as when it strikes objects (with their own added motion), but always measuring the same in seconds of (slower) time from each observer's frame of reference.

All existence is organized energy, demanding intelligent regulation for universal stability. In order to preserve the integrity of matter, the energy of spinning mass requires a regulating constant, which basically is the pre-time force field whose constant nature regulates time to mass. However, I said that the spinning energy that is matter and whose matter is also in motion through space/time is regulated by the time/pressure/gravity phenomenon caused by matter's presence in space/time plus its motion through the dominant regulating pre-time wind. I have claimed that this wind curve of space around matter is time, which exerts varying degrees of pressure on every moving thing in the universe. This phenomenon has been detected in an experiment that contrasted two clocks travelling in nonuniform motion with each other, one in a plane and one on the ground, proving that time does slow down in faster motion.

THE STEADY STATE ACCELERATION EXAMPLE

As matter is moved in a steady state of acceleration, space/time is compressed and acts as gravity, squeezing the spinning energy mass towards a greater than "honest time" light speed. Just like a ball rolling downhill, as mass gathers momentum it tends to spin faster. If this violation of light velocity (within mass) were allowed to stand, it would spin too fast, making mass unstable. Happily, there is an equalizing and stabilizing law of physics: The faster motion of mass, producing the compression of slower time, always equals the need of the velocity of energy in mass as light to remain constant in slower time. In other words, the faster speed in slower time always equals light's constant.

If the earth were catapulted into a steady state of acceleration, we would all experience that extra time distortion of gravity pressure from the direction of the resisting timewind. A voluminous dense body like our earth possesses a gravity equivalent to steady state acceleration. This is because mass displaces space/time by capturing the ether wind (pre-time force), which then compresses in and around mass as the space/time warp pressure of gravity. Hence, for gravity to occur, the earth need not be in a steady state of acceleration because the warped ether wind (pre-time force) presses in equally from all sides, effecting a steady state of pressure, and thus duplicating the gravity effect by the warping of space/time.

In a like manner to steady state acceleration, volume and density effect a similar time/gravity/pressure so that time on a larger planet is slower than time on a smaller planet moving in uniform motion. If one adds the time compression of voluminous mass, squeezing the energy moving within it, to its motion through space (another time compression influence), it will always equal the time/light equation, which is to say, faster light and slower time equals the constant of light speed.

On a mass of sufficient volume the compression can become heat and eventually nuclear ignition. When a voluminous mass is compressed to the point where the energy within it tends to exceed the limit of the time pressure imposed upon it, then the squeezing releases some of the energy bound up in mass as linear radiation, immediately regulated by the push of the ether wind in one direction and the resistance from the other (again the constant). Thus, a star is born.

What if light is fired into infinite space from our newly birthed sun, moving hypothetically at 1,000 miles a minute? Does that mean that the beam of light would move through space forever at 1,000 miles per minute over light speed? No. The timewind resistance coming from the opposite direction would kick in as a regulator.

Thus, the measurement of light velocity will be always the same everywhere in the universe, regardless of the motion of a thousand observers—just as Einstein said. However, my reasons for saying this are different. I believe the motion of anything should be measured not only with respect to another object with greater or lesser motion, but with primal space/time itself. Not just ordinary space/time, mind you, but with a moving space/time that actually has coordinates, bounded by three-dimensional grid-like crisscrossings of pre-time energy/motion, flowing out circumorbitally from the absolute, still, Creation Center of the universe. The (moving) primal stillness is the "birthplace" of physics and of matter, with all its mathematical standards of measurement.

So we conclude here that the whole of space/time is moving with all bodies dragging in space/time with respect to primal stillness. This being the case, again, the interesting news is that the difference between the motion of matter and the motion of space has the potential of imparting usable energy from space/time to matter, gravity being the most obvious case in point, as you will presently see.

Ten

EINSTEIN'S MISSING RELATIVE — GOD

*"We shape the clay into a pot,
but it is the emptiness inside
that holds what we want."*

Lao Tzu

Indeed, the "emptiness" of space holds what we want—for in fact, it is not empty. In his Theory of Relativity, Einstein said that the motion of one object is seen as "motion" only with respect to another object which is said to be at rest; motion is never imputed to an object with respect to space alone. I have added to his position by claiming that not only is the entire universe in motion, but there is also a space/time ether motion flowing over created matter. So while it could be said that an object is at rest (not moving), it is only because science overlooks the key immovable "relative"—the Creator Himself, at absolute rest, with the pre-time force field flowing around Him.

The physics of time, light, matter, and space, once illuminated by one's awakened consciousness of the perfectly still Ultimate Relative, reveals the fascinating reality of a moving space/time ether wind. Perceiving by the light of our inner reality will reveal what should be a self-evident truth—that space/time is actually moving considerably faster than light velocity. This moving space/time may be compared with a car moving with respect to the road; if the road (and, of course, the scenery itself) were to be hypothetically and suddenly made invisible, the car, according to Einstein, would be at rest. But as I see it, this car would in fact still be in motion. Why? Because as I have said, space/time is not a void, but continually flows over matter, which happens to be the reason why matter is matter and remains matter.

Relative to this space "road" (the lines of force we talked about before), instead of the car driving down the road, the road is "driving down the car." The space "road" is there because space/time is moving. Allow me to use a somewhat odd example to illustrate my point. We have all seen the "road racer" type computer game, which challenges a driver's skills by simulating motion. It shows video of a road passing by the motionless driver/player. In this case, the car does not have to drive down the road in order to be "in motion." The road can "drive down the car," causing that relative motion for the benefit of the motionless driver.

Let us transpose this analogy to space/time. I am trying to explain the simple fact that space/time (the road) is actually moving. In space, you may get the impression that you are at rest, but that will be only because you have no visible "road." Of all the miraculous phenomena of creation, space/time is the most elusive, the most difficult to fathom. Space/time is so ethereal, so undetectable as almost to defy scientific scrutiny. It is literally on the border of the metaphysical. Thus, in order to be able to discern space/time motion, one must perceive beyond current knowledge. Searching for such understanding, as Einstein did, one needs illumination from the same Spirit who set creation in motion at that very still beginning. Intuitive scientists like Einstein follow this inner light available to us all.

The idea that motion cannot be seen as motion with respect to space is flawed, unless of course we take the words "be seen" to mean literally that although an object is indeed in motion with respect to moving space/time, it isn't actually "seen" or observed as being in motion.

If, then, the whole of space/time is in motion with no one point in true stillness, then its totality—the whole universe—must have a Relative somewhere to speak its motion into existence, a place of perfect stillness, an absolute rest point defining the true motion of all existence. In fact, this Relative will be found to be the "First Cause" Stillness, the Timeless Origin, the root of all relativities to which everything must be compared, and from which timeless place time itself flows into space/time and hence into all of creation.

Therefore, without this awareness of the Mover (Himself unmoved) by which to observe the whole of existence as moving (floating in rivers of time), any mass parked alone, isolated far enough away from any other object, will always give the impression of stillness because, in and of itself, space conveys no sense of motion to moving objects.

THE QUIET BANG

Mass cannot be the "stillness" that gave it form and function and yet remain mass, any more than a flower made of light can be the sun and remain a flower. Absolute rest is a state that matter cannot experience. Only the soul can experience such stillness, through which, in perfect submission, a new order will descend and modify His creation through an enlightened mankind.

Were all the mass and energy in the cosmos to be gathered in one place, science might well describe that place as one of perfect inertial rest. Why? Because accepted theory says that an object can only be said to be in motion with respect to another object but never with respect to space. If that is so, that alone makes it theoretically impossible for creation to unfold. It is, as I said, not possible for any mass to be perfectly still in space/time because where true inertial stillness is, no matter can exist. Matter is congealed motion out of the truly still "eye" of creation. Motion is creation unfolding and unrolling from the stillness, never again to be as still as the Mover.

Motion (as mass) is expressed from where the Mover sits, Himself unmoved. It is He from whom all things came, the invisible giving form to the visible. Hence we have a "Quiet Bang," a flowing, a stirring out of stillness into motion. Happily, creation came into existence, not as a plasmic singularity that exploded into all the cosmos, but as a flowing, timeless energy field from the metaphysical center of creation.

THE MAGIC OF APPEARING/DISAPPEARING ENERGY

Let's say you were a NASA scientist planning the next Space Shuttle flight and your assignment was to put up in space a satellite that is absolutely still. Could you do it? Of course not, since space/time is, itself, a thing of motion. You could no more put a cork on a rough ocean and have it be still. Let me put it another way. You drive your car to a red light and slow to a stop. Are you really stopped? No, because the earth is rotating. In your car, you cannot be more stopped than stopped, and yet you are moving as fast as the earth is rotating. So when it comes to putting a satellite in space that is absolutely stopped, you must ask yourself where in the universe is anything "stopped."

Since we know that everything moving has a kinetic energy, it can be said that there is a universal kinetic energy that can be tapped. Remember, it doesn't matter whether the car moves down the road or the road moves down the car. That energy is available.

Space is filled with primordial energy (experienced as time/gravity by matter as it drags in the pre-time stream). If this is so—if what I am saying is true—my theory makes possible a remarkable discovery of immense value. If mass does indeed move with respect to (moving) space/time, then it makes not a whit of difference whether mass moves through time or time moves with respect to mass. That mass will have some kind of inherent kinetic energy.

Consider the wind as it blows with respect to a still earth. The air possesses kinetic energy, an energy that wind generators transform into electrical power. Further consider a bullet fired from a rifle; it also possesses kinetic energy. However, once the energy is spent and the bullet lies motionless on the ground, it still possesses kinetic energy because it moves with respect to the earth's surface. Granted the bullet possesses no kinetic energy of its own, but it now shares the motion of the earth. Looking back from space, the earth, itself a kind of bullet, possesses kinetic energy as it hurtles through space; this would be especially notable were the earth to collide with another heavenly body. Kinetic energy has the peculiarity of appearing or disappearing with respect to other bodies, but being everpresent with respect to our enlightened consciousness.

If we could "see" that the earth is moving with respect to space, kinetic energy would then "appear" as a reality, perhaps as a kind of primal wind that could be harnessed to produce safe, usable energy, the way a wind generator produces electricity from the kinetic motion of the wind.

As I said, kinetic energy suddenly appears as if from nowhere with respect to another body in motion. If the earth were to hurtle through space toward another body, the earth's kinetic energy would be dramatically revealed in relationship to that other body. But what if that other body—perhaps a comet—were to be suddenly removed, or if it were to begin traveling in uniform motion with the earth? Would that mean that the "hurtling" earth no longer possesses kinetic energy? Of course not; all motion is relatively still or relatively moving— but moving nevertheless. Only the Mover, Himself perfectly unmoved, can speak motion into existence, and hence creation. All matter is in motion and thus possesses kinetic energy with respect to something—and that something is the second relative of creation, primal physical stillness, the slowest expression of moving space/time. Of course, this whole theory would fall apart without the defining standard of the original metaphysical Stillness, our ultimate missing Relative.

THE ENERGY BEYOND

Wherever a body resides in space, there a time distortion exists and, consequently, a force will be imparted to that body. Think of it—distortion imparting a force to a body! The greater the mass, the greater the force. This force is gravity. In order to be distorted, time/space must be a "something"—something obviously moving and flowing. Otherwise, a body in space would not have anything to interact with or distort.

The awesome force of gravity is not the only example of the energy phenomenon of space/time pressure. The spinning earth with its hot core and magnetic field also comes from this force. Another manifestation of the power of space/time force is the electric field generated by the magnetic rotation of the earth. For example, lightning bolts striking the earth are nothing more than electric current conducted to ground through the superconductor of moist columns of air. Later, I will discuss the connection between space/time, gravity, and magnetic and electric fields.

SUMMARY

Let us review some of these ideas. First: That space/time is not still at all (and therefore is a potential source of energy). Also that matter moves through space/time—or to look at it another way, space/time is moving through matter.

Second: That we can, and should, compare the motion of mass in space with space/time itself, and if we do—by that shift of consciousness alone—we're able to make kinetic energy "appear."

Science accepts that matter is energy, but what many scientists fail to realize is that the "time" aspect of space/time is also energy. In fact, as I have stated repeatedly, it is actually primal energy out of which matter has clotted and is currently dragging in this flowing (pre-time) energy stream we call space/time. Space is not a void, but is filled with this energy, which we must discover philosophically before we can actually find it and use it as an endless, clean resource. Thus, we must first be conscious of its existence and then, and only then, can we consider the practical physics of it.

Eleven

UNIFIED FIELD REVISITED
GRAVITATIONAL, MAGNETIC, AND ELECTRIC

*"Here end my trials for the present. The
results are negative; but they do not shake
my strong feelings of the relation between
gravity and electricity—although they give
no proof that it exists."*

Michael Faraday, Physicist

T*he song of creation is the most beautiful music.
Everywhere, through endless variations, we recognize the
theme of the Composer from the beginning.*

*In the beginning before time began, before God spoke creation
into being, there was "darkness on the face of the deep." And so,
out of the breath of His Spirit a mighty "wind" arose, swirling
out of the stillness. Some of the wind clumped and took form; the
rest flowed on, becoming time to the created things of the wind.*

*The wind moves and yet it is still. It is no thing, yet is many
things; it is both time and timeless.*

*And the "wind" is still blowing faster than we are going; it is
a wind, and yet not a wind—a "no thing," and yet everything.
From nothing came something, from something came everything,
and in everything was everything else.*

*Out of the Stillness came forth timeless motion, and out of
this motion came swirling things. And time came into being as
the motion passed over those things, becoming for them the
wind of time.*

*Out of the Eternal came the infinite external. And so it was
"evening and morning of the first day." There was no solar light
to fill the darkness, but in His wordless way He willed the light to*

be. And so the small gathered and swirled into the big, and into swirling clouds the force of the wind came into the things of the wind and lit a star. And so shone the first light.

And it came to pass that He made countless lights in the firmament, and in these shining furnaces the elements of our earth were made.

And from the earth's star dust, and from the light above, He brought forth life. And the earth He made rotates forever around the light He made for us, as does the universe around the dawn of creation. The Wind of the Spirit still blows, and the creation knows not whence it comes nor whither it goes.

THE MYSTERY OF GRAVITATION

There is much in nature that we take for granted, even though we live among unfathomable mysteries. Gravity is surely the most profound of these. It could well be the primal physical law of all creation. Surely for matter to exist at all it has to hold together. And to hold together, primal energy (primal motion) must become gravity or "gravity/mass."

How does this happen? The sudden, expanding velocity of primal energy gives us our answer. In its steady state of acceleration, primal energy becomes gravity (creates "weight") and at a critical moment converts to mass. The very moment mass exists, it defines a second form of gravity by occupying space and bending the lines of force around it.

I have shown the two ways in which gravity is generated: The first is gravity by steady state acceleration (energy becoming mass) which builds the subatomic microcosm, the smallest of the small. The second gravity exists by virtue of mass occupying and distorting space/time.

We derive our understanding of gravity mostly from large

masses, like planets and stars. Science tells us that mass possesses gravity, and that this gravity bends time. In my view, this is not the case. In fact, it is time that produces gravity by wrapping around the mass. Thus, gravity is not a property of mass; it does not reside there. Rather, mass derives its gravity by curving those pre-time lines of force (time) around it, resulting in pressures against the mass which we call gravity.

The "gravity well" theory does not adequately explain the awesome pressures needed to ignite a star. Gravity, as I said, is the force residing in the surrounding field, transferring its spectacular power to the body's "evolved" relationship with its time/space field origin. Wherever a time distortion occurs, there a force enters the mass as gravity.

TIME DISTORTION PRESSURE

Physicists have not fully grasped the origin of gravity for the simple reason that they assume that gravity is an attribute of mass itself. Thus, in their view, how could gravity possibly pre-exist mass? But gravity in the form of steady state acceleration (Einstein's Equivalence Principle) is actually the primal form of pressure which pre-exists mass and is responsible for the creation of primitive matter.

Please note: This form of gravity is not the one that applies now to existing things. The moment mass exists, clotted out of this original pressure force, a second kind of gravity applies itself. The pre-creation force immediately surrounds and compresses in on mass, manifesting as a push force (gravity) as in the case of the push force of a stream on a rock. Remember, there are two principles at work here: One is steady state acceleration pressure and the other is simply a steady pressure affecting mass— mass now bathed in the flow of its own primal energy origin.

The bending of this flow of pre-time energy around mass (like the stream around the rock) is what science identifies as time ("Mass warps time"). However, from my point of view it is not only time, but time distortion pressure, and hence gravity.

The gravitational field of subatomic particles is similar to that of true mass in this way. As super-accelerated pre-time energy from the metaphysical dimension is spun fast enough, it clumps itself into this dimension as minute particles in time.

The gravitational form of these particles is sustained by means of continued motion through the wind of pre-time force from which they came (now timewind pressure). Thus, by the apparent velocity of these original particles (their spinning and dragging in the three-dimensional timewind), a distortion of space/time around each one occurs, producing an effect in the microcosm similar to that of a large mass. Consequently, none of these particles, pushed and regulated by the pre-time wind, can move slower than the speed of light. Their motion is certainly not one of their own making

Visualize, if you will, a tiny primal particle made of compressed "swirling wind" being spun like a top (inwardly) by the force of what becomes to it a timewind. Imagine the origitron as a little "dust devil," gathering form by way of its swirling motion and becoming a kind of primitive mass by its resistance to motion. Or think of it as an eddy in the water: The water motion makes the spin, and it *is the spin*. These two forms (the water motion and the eddy) of the one force eventually become all the forms of creation. After the eddy is formed out of the water motion, it is the water's motion that keeps the eddy spinning. In a similar way the origitron gets its spinning form and keeps its form by way of the ever-flowing pre-time force.

The spinning of the origitron and its velocity through space distorts space/time and becomes its sustaining gravity. Its spinning becomes the magnetic field around it and, in turn, the motion of this now-magnetic particle becomes the electric field around it. The same order occurs with true mass: first, gravitational; second, magnetic; and last, electric. Magnetic because it spins and electric because it moves while spinning. A moving magnetic field always creates an electric field.

Alignment of Atoms Causes Planets to Rotate

When a sufficient portion of the core of any mass becomes solid due to the pressure of gravity, atoms align, producing the almost perfect magnetic field. Collectively, *en masse*, the aligned atoms then tend to spin all in the same general direction, causing the whole body to rotate, thus producing an electric field as it moves through the ether.

If it were possible to stop the earth and then leave it "still" in space, the earth would once again start rotating, all by itself. It would, however, be rotating by a power derived from its gravity-induced core alignment, which makes the earth a perpetual-motion generator. The earth's iron core becomes a crystalline solid under compression, surrounded by iron in its molten state. The solid core spins in this thick soup faster than the earth's surface, dragging the earth around more slowly with it. A similar process with other elements causes other heavenly bodies (planets, moons, stars) to rotate.

Magnetic Fields Produce Electric Fields

Contrary to the traditional view of lightning, I believe that wherever a column of moist air possesses sufficient density and reaches high enough into the atmosphere, the everpresent electric charge surrounding our planet is conducted to ground as lightning bolts. It has been said that one such bolt has enough energy to light up a small city. Flying under the conditions that might produce a lightning storm, pilots see this electric charge, stored in cloud formations, manifest itself as a strange glow on the aircraft's wing tips and as fiery displays dancing across the windscreens known as Saint Elmo's fire.

Tornadoes may in fact be caused, not by conflicting hot and cold rising currents of air, but by the arcing to earth of one or more lightning bolts. That is to say, a steady, long-lasting lightning flash which causes a vacuum to be filled in by a swirling rush of air. It is likely that Nikola Tesla knew about this abundant energy source when he said he could deliver free energy to every home without wires. At the time, this claim was considered fantasy, but in the 21st Century it may at last become reality.

Twelve

THE PRE-BANG VOID

*"And the earth was
without form and void;"*

Genesis 1:2

Before we tackle the problem of the Void we need to better understand the nature of space/time distance. Space/time is not a void; it possesses energy, which is time flowing into distance over mass. On the other hand, the Void contains no time, no distance, and no space. I know it is hard to imagine a true void; it surely is almost beyond our comprehension. The Void is infinitely cold, a spaceless space, a distanceless distance. In a sense, the Void is massless "solid."

Were it possible to accelerate a spacecraft beyond light velocity, space/time would disappear and the physical dimensions of matter would become zero. At that point, you would literally hit a wall of resistance, because matter, for the lack of space, would be squeezed out of existence. While this wall of resistance might very well be the resisting pre-time wind, beyond that wall could be the Void. In any case, at that velocity there would be no space, no time, and no length—but there would still be motion. This is as close to a void as you can get, but it would not be the Void. In a true void there is no motion and no energy. We cannot create a void or an absolute zero because everywhere, no matter how minute, exists God's creation, which precludes the possibility of an absolute zero cold. Thus we can never experimentally reach a true void. After all, what is there to understand about the Void? Nothing—except that it "was" before the beginning. However, this book would be remiss were it to neglect attempting to describe the pre-creation state, which even most secular scientists know must have existed.

According to the third law of thermodynamics it is not possible to reach absolute zero temperature, taking as it does longer and longer to reach lower and lower temperatures as absolute zero is approached. In other words, if it could happen, it would take forever. Likewise, practically speaking, there is just not enough energy available to reduce space/time to a zero point.

Contemporary science has accepted the notion that the lingering ambient temperature of the known universe is the residual heat of the Big Bang, but I think not. Rather, I believe it is the energy presence of motion, the pre-time force, the potential energy of which converts to gravity heat with regard to mass and consequently the nuclear fusion of all stars. Therefore space/time is not a void; it can never be because it possesses the motion of the mysterious energy of creation—a creation that everpresently awaits its birth into matter.

Nevertheless, to understand the Void we need to revisit the concept of space/time to get a clearer view of what distance is, simply because the Void has no distance (no length in any direction). It has no substance and no energy flows. It is a cold, massless "solid."

The "space" that once existed before time is the Void. Nothing existed and nothing could. Before existence and before time there came to be a flowing river of pure energy from which matter came. And then time began to flow like a river from a hidden timeless source; we now exist in its endless flow. Point in any direction and that is a dimension of distance, and flowing over us into distance as time is the endless flowing current. The endless flowing over us is time's present moment, flowing on into the infinity of immeasurable distance.

So fast is this river that nothing can equal the speed of its current. No matter how fast you move, the current moves faster past you (as time) into distance ahead. Ahead is the infinity of distance, and distance is the endless length of the river's flowing beyond.

The more we move towards infinity, the more the length of the river's distance moves infinitely ahead of our efforts. After having flowed over us as time's present moment, its distance becomes the river's infinite length, always stretching infinitely ahead. Therefore we cannot arrive at the end of this flow unless we are able to move at least as fast as the flow, so as to cause the flowing to stop moving past us.

Time and distance can be compared with an endless tape measure being pulled out ahead of a runner, much faster than he can go. This analogy relates to an object moving in time trying to catch up to distance. What if our runner could catch up to the speed of the measuring tape so that it no longer shoots out ahead of him? The once impossibly distant measurement of the tape would then be running right next to him in the form of a "stationary" mark on the tape. That would be the end of his measuring distance, being equivalent to the end of the journey through space/time/distance.

Were we to travel through space/time forever, we would never arrive at the end of the river's infinitely flowing length. There is no final resting place, no destination, no place to stop, no matter how far we go, since distance itself is the measure of the stretch of the river ahead, ever flowing over us as time into infinity. Were it possible to accelerate, like that runner, equal to the current flowing over us, a remarkable thing would happen. As we reached the velocity equal to the river's flow, suddenly there would be no flowing over us as time, hence no more time and no more distance ahead.

Distance and time are really the measurement of the speed of our traveling through the infinite length of the ever-flowing river current. Therefore, when no more river is flowing over us into the beyond, there is no more beyond for us. There is also no more time for us and hence no more distance to go.

Let us pretend we could undertake such a journey and pretend also that it is scientifically feasible to travel way beyond the velocity of light and still exist. Before leaving on this fictitious journey, let's say we set our alarm clock to ring 12 hours hence at 12 midnight Earth time. Now we accelerate our spacecraft into the length of current flowing over us as time/distance ahead. A strange thing begins to happen just as Einstein predicted it would. We notice our clock is running slower compared to our standard of "Earth time." The faster we move through this ever-flowing length of the river, the slower our on-board clock ticks. You see, the clock is measuring our progress toward the end of time's flowing over us into distance. Remember that distance is measured by our motion through the current. Too slow, and the "infinite distance" moves infinitely ahead. Our clock would run forever measuring it, and the reason for this is that time is still passing over, going on into the infinity of length. So there is always a measure of length going ahead to be measured in (faster or slower) time.

Only when we attain and maintain a speed equal to the current will there be no more flowing of time over us as distance ahead. Only if this were to happen could we arrive at the end of time's space/distance, not able to proceed any further. It is the wall. The ship's clock has stopped at 10 minutes to midnight because there is no more journey, no more flowing of time into distance. All is dead still. Nothing moves—nothing can move. There is no space. There is no length. All this accomplished by moving faster than the speed of light. And yet, at this point, we have still not reached the Void. Why? Because there is still motion.

THE ABSOLUTE VOID

Whereas time is the flowing river of energy, flowing over mass into infinite distance, and whereas distance is the endless "beyond" of the river flowing over and beyond mass, the Void has no flowing energy. It is hence a distanceless, massless, energyless "solid." If the river we experience as time would stop flowing, we would not need the acceleration process equal to its flow to come to the end of distance in time, simply because mass would cease to exist and time would stop. There would then be no more distance to go because there would be no more motion. Remember, motion is what distance is as it passes as time over mass.

There are two ways for time and distance to stop and for matter to no longer exist: One is to catch up to the river of pre-time force, and the other is for the river of pre-time force, itself, to cease flowing. However, when God acted on the frozen, massless "solid" of the Void, it "melted" everywhere at once as might a frozen river exposed to heat everywhere at once. God's motion acts on the Void as a "heat" to the absolute cold. The Void then is a dimensionless, pure nothing, empty of motion. It is like a solid which prevents any motion within it.

The force of the pre-time river, while being ethereal and moving billions of times faster than the speed of light, is also billions of times thinner than wind. The primal wind is a primal motion, a "fluid" in which things exist, move, and "swim." If the wind were to cease, there would be once again the infinite, massless, frozen Void. Nothing moves, nothing exists to move, and nothing could move even if there were something to move. The Void is infinitely black, infinitely cold, infinitely motionless; there is no distance, because there is no time to go anywhere. "There" would be "here," and "here" is nowhere. *And so the Lord God moved upon the frozen waters of the Void, and they melted in His presence. Immediately, they began to flow.*

"In the beginning of creation when God made Heaven and earth, the earth was without form and void, and darkness was on the face of the abyss. And a mighty wind swept over the surface of the waters and God said, *Let there be light...*"

Thirteen

TIME
THE MYSTERIOUS FOURTH DIMENSION

*"I shall never believe that God
plays dice with the world."*

Albert Einstein

The laws of physics are defined in very precise language, mostly mathematics. Before the equations of science existed, there had to be theory. Scientists have zealously sought to discover a unified field theory of matter, a single common principle underlying all things. But so far they have failed. It is my belief that once the fundamental law governing matter is understood, then all the laws that spring from it will harmonize, having not only complete scientific relevance but also metaphysical meaning.

The four dimensions of length, width, depth, and time are not really four distinct dimensions, but are woven out of just one—that which we sense as time.

Even more astonishing, you will discover that time (if you go back far enough) is not originally a dimension either. "Time" existed only in an extra-dimensional pre-time state as lines of pre-physical force originating from and circumorbiting a still creation event. And this force still flows the same way today from that dimension into this one. Time exists even now in both states at once, depending on the frame of reference with respect to matter.

Let me again illustrate the unfolding cosmological order of the creation by using a length of string to make the point. Let us proceed to wind the string into a ball. Starting at the "still" center with a single strand, round and round we go, the motion of the string (representing the flow of force) weaving about itself a body that would never have existed without the winding motion. The more string we use, the bigger the ball grows. In a similar fashion, our entire universe comes into existence as a sphere with a curved, infinitely expanding horizon. What we experience as time in this dimension is simply those curved lines of force (like the motion of the string), flowing from (and around) the timeless center and taking form. They weave their never-ending invisible threads, coming from every direction at once, into an infinitely expanding universe. Time eventually becomes the fourth dimension in the very process of its weaving.

Actually, at first "time" has no more real dimension than that string in our illustration before it forms itself into a string ball. Time is the essential motion that plays the role of the other three dimensions as it continues to shape the expanding, spherical universe.

Time, then, is simply pre-time lines of force circumorbiting in a way similar to the making of a string ball, flowing out of a creation event center with incomprehensible velocity, millions, perhaps even billions of times the speed of light. Who could measure it? Especially since real time measurement won't come into existence until matter appears, and thus defines it.

You will recall my description of how energy matter is "clumped" out of those very same lines of force, which I named pre-time force. Such lines of force do not exist as time without real matter to give pre-time force its time factor relativity to matter. As pre-time force gives birth to matter, only then does it become time in relation to the three-dimensional matter it birthed.

Remember how matter clotting out of pre-time force lags behind in the "wind" of pre-time's flowing? Well, that is exactly what time is: the wind of pre-time's flowing, only as experienced by matter. And since the lines of force I am describing come from every direction "at once" (because of the explosive, supernatural speed of their circumorbiting pattern), it follows that matter "clotting" out of such lines of force spins three-dimensionally.

So then, length, width, and depth are simply one and the same aspect of the lines of force becoming the fourth dimension of time to what has become three-dimensional mass in space/time.

Bear in mind that the pre-time force energy "string" alone is not a dimension; time cannot be a dimension of time to itself any more than the length of string is a ball before it winds around itself, going round and round. The ball is the "dimension" that the movement of the string has formed. Without the round and round motion, the string would have no dimension beyond "string."

Understand that the string analogy is as close as I can get to the point I am making. Granted, real string has its own dimensions. However the pre-time "string(s)," the lines of force I am describing, have no dimension but are just pure lines of force, circumorbitally enlarging the invisible, spherical boundaries of what we now call the universe, fashioning also the three dimensions of matter clotted from this force. When the lines of force flow over mass, causing that mass to lag back (like a log in a stream), and then they pass beyond it, they create distance in three-dimensional time/space—hence length, width, and depth, and obviously time.

If we could become totally objective and stand outside our present existence, we would see time not as a dimension, but only as a force—a field emanating from (and orbiting) a dimension other than our own.

Time is no more time to itself than the motion of the wind is wind to itself. If air blows past something slower than itself, then it becomes wind to that object but it can never be wind to itself. So time (like the pre-time lines of "string") is just a metaphysical motion. How then shall time be a measurement to itself? To move equal with time is to experience no motion at all. Hence at that point there would be no time at all, just as when something moves at the same rate and in the same direction as a wind, it experiences no wind at all.

Time itself exists as a dimension only after the pre-time lines of force have shaped the other three, and given birth to matter lagging behind in this pre-time "wind;" then and only then does time become the fourth dimension to the other three.

Matter is essential for the pre-time "wind" force to exist as space/time in relation to matter. In order to complete the picture of creation, it is imperative to have energy/mass in three-dimensional space/time. Without the presence of mass (length, width, depth), time has no meaning or relevance. Three-dimensional bodies exist as creation fallout, shaped by and dragging in what is now timewind coming from all directions.

THE MIND WITHIN THE FORCE

Consider how electrons circumorbit the nucleus of an atom, changing course like the winding string. They do not revolve flat like the rings of Saturn. They circumorbit in a way that gives the atom its three-dimensional form in time. Thus do all orbiting electrons mimic the shape of the universe, most likely influenced to orbit in their three-dimensional circumorbiting manner by the very three-dimensional motion of "time" itself. As such, the universe is not just a physical reaction playing itself out, but is more a metaphysical phenomenon, ever responding to the pulse of God-force. In other words, the cosmos is constantly alive to His Will.

Length, width, and depth in energy/mass are all woven out of the strands of this one physical/metaphysical pre-time force (time to us), circumorbiting a still creation event. All is one and one is all. The whole of creation comes from the spiritual dimension; everything is indeed everything else. As I've said before, from the "wind of no thing" came the "somethings" and from somethings came everything, and so in everything was also everything else.

Space is filled with motion, the invisible, timeless "mother" force which is also time to her creations, ever weaving her three-dimensional nest, continually giving birth to matter in three-dimensional space in never-ending time.

At the beginning of creation, there were only "threads" of pre-time timeless motion, super-energized and whirling around the One centered in the still eye of creation. If we could go further back than creation, we would go to that place whence God spoke out of His Stillness, "Let there be..."

Fourteen

BACK TO THE FUTURE
THE UNIFIED FIELD, ALPHA TO OMEGA

*"The laws of physics seem
themselves to be the product
of exceedingly ingenious design."*

British astrophysicist Paul Davies

I have said that the universe and all that it contains operates somewhat like a radar screen with an energy field flowing out of a still center, going round and round (in three dimensions), leaving little glowing blips (of matter) trailing "phosphorescent-ly," all being renewed with every sweep of the force field.

All that existed immediately before the creation of matter was a moving energy field swirling about the Primal Rest. But in the very beginning, there existed only the First Cause Rest—Who first caused motion, generating that energy field that had not yet defined the dimensions nor become *bona fide* creation. Then as creation began to materialize from this first energy field into what became the second one, matter clotted out of this motion and was left trailing behind the "sweeping energy field."

Considering my illustration of the radar screen, visualize the two coexisting yet distinct dimensions. The first (spiritual), from which creation later descends, is the realm of primal motion, caused by that swirling "field arm" connected to the still "hub" at the center of the cosmos.

The second field consists of the physical dimension (of matter) which exists lagging behind that swirling field (or the glowing arm of the radar screen). Just as with blips on a radar screen, creation's "blips" (new particles) are sustained with each pass of the force field "arms."

In essence, there are two fields (dimensions) coexisting, one within the other, the original timeless field "giving birth" to its time-bound creation field and sustaining it in its flowing time.

The "blips" on the "screen" represent primal matter clotting out of pre-time energy and dropping out, as it were, from the timeless motion of the primal field, and lagging three-dimensionally in space/time, time being the fourth dimension.

THE BORDER

Therefore all of physics can be reduced to a single field— the timeless one, just before creation, that we cannot directly experience. That same field in the same instant also represents time to the matter clotted out of it. Thus the procession of laws that we call physics is born of and linked to the pre-physical field described above.

Remember that if you accelerate in any one of the three dimensions in present time, try as you may to catch up to those sweeping lines of pre-time force, you will not be able to—partly because time will begin to slow and eventually stand still, and also because matter in its three dimensions of space/time would cease, having been "squeezed" out of existence. Nevertheless, whatever is left of us (not that anything could exist) would still be moving at incredible velocity, yet without the need for space/time. This is without question the uncrossable border. Beyond this frontier is "the timeless stillness that moves," the moving force field, emanating from and circumorbiting the absolutely still Creation Center, a mysterious timeless realm which is the purest form of motion, where creation perpetually awaits its birth.

I cannot emphasize this point often enough. Science will never be able to push matter fast enough (or slow enough) to cross this boundary and go back to the other side where there are no physical sciences. The other side is the spiritual dimension from which the whole of the physical universe came, including science itself.

More about the Two Fields

It is theoretically possible to reduce all of physics to the one field we've been discussing. The metaphysical field is essential to the physical one, because the physical field has descended from the metaphysical. The physical field is sustained by the action of the metaphysical field, both having a common center in the Perfect Creation Stillness.

So the whole of physics owes its existence to the materialization of energy/mass emerging from the pre-physical pre-time (motion) field, both coexisting and connected to the hub, the eye of absolute stillness around which swirls the storm of timeless time and real time.

Obviously, we exist only in the second dimension, made vital by the first one, the metaphysical dimension that continuously sweeps over us with infinite velocity, going beyond as infinite time and distance. The spiritual dimension, then, everpresently surrounds creation and infuses it with energy.

All that which is purely physical exists in time present, but that which is also spiritual (man) lives in the Timeless Presence as well. To spiritual mankind, time present and the Timeless Presence overlap and coexist. The fact that the spirit coexists with the flesh—that it occupies the same space as the material body— creates a friction that is experienced as conflict and guilt, a travail like a woman in labor. The soul, coexisting in the body, has allegiances—either to the flesh, which is subject to the external forces of nature from the beginning of time, or to the Source of all creation, He that existed before time began and abides within us now. So you can see there is no tangible answer to the question: "Where is the soul in the body?" It is both there and not there, because it coexists in two dimensions at once.

Therefore is the cosmos an inter-dimensional phenomenon, an outpouring of Divine Energies into the physical realm, allowing the Spirit of God to enter into His "creature image" of Himself upon the completion of His work. For the temple of God is man, created in His likeness. Man's soul, then, stands astride two worlds, between the forces of good and evil, time-lessness and time. If a man submits himself to the moral impulses of the Timeless One, then time is under his feet; he ceases to be subject to tyrannical time that rules over the rest of mankind. Therefore, if man surrenders his spirit in helplessness and humility, he will exist in a state described in religious parlance as "saved," and thus live on eternally with God. The physically uncrossable border is crossed.

DEADLY GRAVITATIONS

Man is born first of the lineage of nature and then of spirit. Although we are composed both of nature and of spirit, our souls must yearn to resolve the mystery of our captivity to the (animal) flesh, which is inherently and genetically subject to all the grav-itations of physical laws from the beginning of time when God said, "Let there be." Read on carefully, my friend; persevere, and you will soon come to know this mystery. For we are dealing with a subtle and malevolent spirit working through our pride, a spirit that keeps us not only subject to the body's dissolution, but beyond that also to the death of our souls. So you see, it is not just a matter of being inevitably subject to change, decay, and death, like the beast of the field. Rather, our life and death have to do with a factor that is not inevitable, namely the inclination of our egos toward the self-centeredness of the pride of life—in other words, toward evil. So that when this terrible, self-destructive inclination has divided us from the Father within, we then experience death both in nature and in Spirit.

Should we be content to breed, wither, and die, circling a star with the universe itself, rotating endlessly around the dawn of creation? Do our souls have another beginning at the end of this life? Surely our yearning and our longings tell us there are two possible origins in the way we exist: the one we fell from and the one we fell into. Can we "live in the world and yet not be of it?" Can we be born in one world and then be reborn into another? Surely the friction within our souls is telling us there is something wrong with this meaningless life, that we have somehow missed the return cycle of the soul's completion.

Somewhere in here lies the mystery of the "two lives," the two choices our Heavenly Father has given us—to love Him or to deny Him. The human family, having pridefully fallen from unity with Him into division, lives unnaturally in the natural world. In other words, our egos inherit disunity and exist self-destructively as unnatural subjects of the natural world. However, if we are willing, we can live as we were meant to live—spiritually in the natural world He created for us, that is, without ego separation from our Creator who from the beginning has prepared a way back for us.

MOTHER NATURE/FATHER GOD

The field from which matter emerges not only "mothers" and sustains matter, but "she" does something much more astounding. She gives her creations their functional identity in a step-by-step process of cause and effect. A clear example of this phenomenon, based on the unified field theory presented in this book, can be found in the following sequence. Primal matter is birthed from the "mother field," and so is time and gravity pressure. As gross matter congeals under pressure, stars and planets are born, and under the steady pressure of the field's force, larger planetary cores become molten. The intense pressure/heat crystallizes the center of the molten core which, in turn, causes the magnetic field to spin—and from this movement comes the electric field. Here, in this sequence, we have a good example of how the creation entrains itself back to the "creator" mother field, one of millions such examples. The creation of the electric field is a typical expression of how the whole process unfolds.

In the womb a baby is called a fetus; when it is born it's known as an infant, then it grows into a toddler, and then, one day, the infant's mother finds herself looking at a teenager. Eventually the teenager presents himself to the parents as a mature adult. In a similar way, all the photons, electrons, and atoms, with their various numbers, forms, and motions are presented back to the mother field that birthed them. It is "she" who actually gives them their identities, their chemistries, their functions, their laws, and their behaviors. They are hydrogen; they are oxygen; they are gold; they are planets; they are stars. So you see that while matter has various forms, motions, orbits, and cycles, it is the field from which they came that also "names" them. It is the "mother" field that endows them with their behaviors, numbers, and chemistries. (Some readers may prefer to think of it as a "Son" field; either way the physical function is the same.)

Matter not only comes from the field, but also is defined by the field. The mother field comes from God, Who connects Himself, through the medium of "her" field, to all things He has created and made through her. The field in which we are submerged (time present) therefore is to us the mother of all natural identities. At each stage of all her manifestations, mother insinuates herself into the predestined forms of matter in motion, and imputes to them their particular identities. The field in which all creation is submerged is passing over us as time, and is in continuous contact with Him, Who speaks through her to all His creation. He commands her to give birth to all creation and, through her, gives all things their instincts, their magical chemistries, and their auras with which to move and have their existence, their aliveness and "beingness." (For us, though, we need the imprint *not of creation,* but of the timeless Identity received from the Creator Himself.)

Science asks the question: Can we reject the concept of matter and energy and build a pure field theory of physics? The answer is yes; in a manner of speaking we can. Remember, without the evolution of matter from the mother field, creation would have no expression, no form or function. Matter is really a physical expression of the mother field, which in turn is the expression of the Father at the center of "the All."

While the field can exist without matter, matter would perish without the field. And, of course, God exists without the "mother field" but the "mother field" would collapse without His sustaining force. Matter then, is the expression of both fields (physical and metaphysical) in all their glorious forms; one dimension extending into the other has become creation. And without Him, all things will collapse into nothingness. "The whole universe has been created through and for Him." Col., 1:16 (NEB)..."and they all in Him hold together." Col. 1:17 (ENT).

Atoms have a nucleus surrounded by a field—as do all the lesser particles whose centers and fields give them their identities. The field surrounding the nucleus of an atom mirrors the universe as does the "mother nature" field of our nature, revolving about the Still Spirit of the Father God, who, through her, gave form to matter and all the things of creation.

THE FIFTH DIMENSION

Space/time is the massless mother field. Before creation, "she" is pure pre-time energy in motion, circumorbiting the Father God. Then, upon Divine command, being hurled into the Void, her energy clots as energy/mass and begins creation. It is the mother field that spawns energy/mass, leaving all her spinning creations entrained in her field, which flows over them as time. "Her" very presence (actually time present) is the living force for all the phenomena of the cosmos. Her energy is everpresent, all around, flowing over everything as time—time present—which for all creation represents the Alpha and Omega, the beginning and the end.

In nature, alpha/omega is death and rebirth, the passing of the seasons; whereas human alpha/omega is dying to this life to be born again, saved from death, raised up and renewed by the spirit to real life. Thus, in the truest sense, man is capable of dying to death; in other words, for the seeking soul there is no death, and time is timeless.

Time is more than just time. It is a field. It is energy before matter. It is pre-time before time before matter. Whatever name we give to it, it is a metaphysical field surrounding the Creator before creation and a physical field to creation. Matter is connected to the mother and the mother to the Father; the Father is the metaphysical center of all, defining all through the mother.

So what is proclaimed here, in somewhat nonscientific terms, is a unified field theory—not just one field, but two— the metaphysical giving birth to the physical. My friend, if you can see to the root truth of this, forsake the love of creation— the world—and exchange it for the love of the Creator of the world, and receive His saving grace. Continue not in your own will, but abide in His. Come back to your future, to the Timeless Everpresence.

CROSSING THE MORAL BORDER

Although many of us lead lives of rush and distraction, "steady state acceleration" never got anyone anywhere. The pure of heart have no need to voyage or hurry, but should rather slow down and find the still place within. For such as these, "there" is also "here" in the everpresent stillness of the now. With the dissolution of the body, they merely step across the border. Spirit is inter-dimensional while matter is not. Spirit can enter into and coexist with matter, but matter itself can never go back and enter into spirit.

Be warned, do not run from the stillness. That is to say, be careful not to descend egocentrically, to wallow sensually in the passions of your flesh, lest you lose your spiritual life, exchanging it for the ego-animal one that cannot cross over. Awaken, running man, from your sensual sleep of escape and, before it's too late, find the purpose for which you were created.

Fifteen

WHY GRAVITY IS REALLY PUSHY
A NEW THEORY OF SPONTANEOUS CREATION

*"The shocking thing is that there
seems to be an absolute axis, a kind
of cosmological north star that
orients the universe."*

Physicist Borge Nodland, 1997

The most subtle, highest, purest form of anything is the ether field; it is the quintessence of energy mass, the precursor to matter. The ether is the unified field out of which everything is created without the need for a Big Bang "singularity."

Let me bring forward the main problem associated with believing that the universe began with an explosive "singularity," something infinitely hot, dense, and small. The problem is gravity. If, as contemporary science holds, gravity is a pulling attribute of matter, then indeed there are very serious problems with time preceding the creation event. Why? Because, as I said in the opening chapter, time would be incapable of escaping the phenomenal gravity of so dense a mass. The primeval gravitational pull would have been so enormous there never would have been a creation event because that would have required the dimension of time in order to go "Bang."

I firmly believe that gravity has no pull, nor is it an attribute of matter. There is absolutely no gravitational force tugging on all the matter in the universe, pulling it all back to its beginning singularity. In fact, according to this new theory, gravity is not only not a force weighing the universe down, it is the vital pre-time force flinging the cosmos out in a continuously flowing creation event.

Gravity as Newton described it did not originally exist. Granted, time needs to exist in the birthing of creation, but time did not need to precede creation. As I have said, time actually appeared immediately and spontaneously with the clumping of matter, resulting from the out-flinging of the ether field. This happened when the "no thing" of the ether (the pre-time force) became the "something" of matter in space/time with gravity. Allow me to be repetitive; this is so important.

The essence of time, and of everything, is this unified ether field, which I have named pre-time force, a pre-physical force out of which subatomic particles are created under pressure, dragging slower than the force itself. In this way does the unknowable pre-time force become knowable as time to mass as it flows over mass in space. Without this clumping of primitive particles of matter out of the pre-physical force, time would not be time; it would remain as the primitive and peculiar motion of pure energy, pre-existent and metaphysical.

As matter is created, and hence occupies space/time, what appears (relative to mass) as the time dimension becomes curved instantly, warped by the newly created occupant of space/time. As you will see, this warping or curving of the force compresses immediately in on matter as a push pressure.

In this construction, gravity occurs only with respect to time's relevance to matter. In other words, the same force that creates matter also becomes time factor to matter, and matter warping this space/time force causes the compression on matter as a push/pressure, hence gravity.

Again, may I submit that gravity is not an attribute of matter, but of matter's relationship with the same force from which matter is birthed along with time itself.

BIG BANG WITH A TWIST: AN INSTANT UNFOLDING

As you will see, time does not need to precede any creation event as currently theorized in the "Big Bang" postulate. On the contrary, space/time and hence distance are created simultaneously with three-dimensional matter; thus all four dimensions are satisfied from the one primal force.

The essential point here is that the basic substance, the "clay" of all creation, is instantaneously created, rather than evolving from a chain of events. Descartes said it perfectly: Without matter, space (space/time) is unthinkable. In the absence of matter— in a pre-time realm of pure, pre-physical energy—time is not yet time, and hence there can be no distance and no gravity. Space/time, matter, and gravity are inseparable and coexistent, simultaneously birthed from what appears to be empty space.

EXPLAINING THE UNEXPLAINED FORCE

In what has become known as the Equivalence Principle, Einstein stated that gravity is indistinguishable from "steady state acceleration." A good example of this is the G-force felt by astronauts blasting off, or the pressure you feel against your feet on a fast, upward-accelerating elevator. As long as there is steady acceleration, the gravity equivalence is experienced, not as a pull but as a push, a downward pressure.

To understand this, we need only to refer to Isaac Newton's underlying principle, which is that for every motion there is an equal and opposite motion. Resistance resulting from the opposing motion is the force that presses astronauts against their seats, just as you are pressed against the elevator floor.

So as I previously said, the greater the force exerted against a body, the more that body will weigh; twice the acceleration would double the opposing force. A cannonball, under these conditions, would weigh twice as much and so, of course, would a feather; each would have a "weight" proportionate to its mass times the downward pressure upon it.

However, as any scientist can tell you, the earth is not in a steady state of acceleration around the sun; if it were, we would feel this gravity from only one direction, the direction of the earth's acceleration.

Gravity, however, is a relatively even force all around the earth and that doesn't exactly describe a "steady state" phenomenon; thus, we have falsely assumed gravity to be not a pressing force but rather some kind of attracting force, a "pulling in" caused somehow by the mass of the earth itself. Here scientists made a classic mistake common to research: They drew the wrong conclusion for lack of a key element; they missed the right principle (pressing force gravity), because they rejected the idea of a cosmic ether. Obviously, without the existence of an ether force the pushing force principle could never apply; thus, they looked elsewhere and theorized a pulling force, the only other choice. However, once the ether force is understood, the push-force gravity theory becomes workable. More than that, the ether force theory is the missing link that unifies the creative logic of the whole universe.

GRAVITY—A NEW THEORY

Science has theories pertaining to gravity, some of them right and some wrong. In my opinion, the closest science has come to a unified gravity theory is Einstein's Equivalence Principle, the force of steady state acceleration. However, as I have said, there is one important missing link in scientists' collective thinking about "steady state." Although they recognize the kind of gravity represented by the Equivalence Principle, they haven't been able to apply it properly, simply because they rejected the existence of an ether force, the very thing that could have explained the pressing force theory of gravity. I am proposing here a new theory of gravity, based on pressing force.

The two currently accepted gravity principles are: First, steady state acceleration (the kind of downward force we have all experienced in the upward motion of an elevator). As Einstein said, this resulting "downward force" acts like gravity. However, what makes it unique to an understanding of "creation out of nothing" is that this kind of gravity does not require mass, but figures in the creation of mass. When an unlimited force is thrust into an environment of limits, resistance is created—and this resistance creates gravitational pressure which, in turn, creates primordial mass. Thus, we have "primal gravitation," the steady state acceleration force that brings matter into existence.

How does the acceleration pressure of primal gravitation relate to the gravity phenomenon of planetary objects, which we know are not accelerating? The answer is that it doesn't. Steady state theory doesn't need to apply beyond the creation of original mass—for once mass has been created, it sets up a new gravitational dynamic. This is the second principle. We no longer need steady state acceleration; what we need is a simple steady state of pressure—a leveling off of the initial rush of force which becomes a constant pressure, acting on the mass that was created from that original "steady state acceleration." Again, steady state acceleration provides only the necessary initial pressure; once mass is created, it is not acceleration that's required, but simply the warped time/pressure aspect relating to mass.

The accepted second principle is that gravity warps space/time. However, it is my opinion that it is not gravity that warps space/time; rather it is space/time warping around mass that causes a pressure or push gravity. Once we accept the existence of an ether force (that space is not nothing), the right conclusion about the gravity phenomenon is inescapable. Like the rock in the stream, we have a steady state of pressure on planetary mass—not steady state acceleration, but a continuous pressure nonetheless.

Ironically, the man who discovered gravity, Sir Isaac Newton, expressly contradicted the currently accepted notion that bodies exert an attraction upon one another. He insisted that bodies only acted *as if* they were attracted to one another in accordance with the law of the inverse square of the distance.

In a 1935 book entitled *Le Grand Secret de L'univers,* the French author and scientist Cambell expressed the belief that "cosmogenic waves," as he called them, had the capacity to exert a push against matter; furthermore, he thought that those waves moved with equal force everywhere from all possible directions simultaneously.

Let us ponder these theories in greater detail. Imagine if you will a tiny pebble in a rushing stream. Compare the pressure on one side of the pebble to the same pressure against a boulder. Clearly, by its greater size the larger rock captures more of the rushing energy of the flowing stream.

Now imagine (what we experience as) time itself as an invisible stream rushing past that boulder (for example, a planet) with an infinite velocity from all directions at once. Can you conceive how the presence of a massive object like a planet would curve the flow of those "time lines of force" around it, absorbing pressure just the way the boulder does in the stream?

The bigger the mass, the more it will experience the space/time "fluid" pressure around it. Such pressure is actually a transference of energy from the rushing space/time medium to a planet or star or other mass. With the rushing stream I used as an illustration you have only a finite energy moving against the rock, but with the infinite velocity of space/time force, billions of times the speed of light, there is an infinite potential pressure upon any mass relative to its volume and density.

Let me restate it: The bigger the mass, the greater the potential "time" warp pressure against the curve of the mass, and hence the greater the transfer of that pressure (energy) to it. Consider now our own planet with pressures converging from all sides toward the center of its mass with such compression as to heat its core. The hot center of the earth is not just left-over heat from some prehistoric radioactive formation, but will forever remain molten by virtue of those pressures continually exerted upon it by the forces described in this chapter. The larger the mass, the greater the pressure, enough pressure even to ignite a star.

Another French scientist, Pierre Simone Marquis de la Place, in his book, *Traitise sur la Théorie de la Mécanique Céleste,** visualized gravity as a push produced by the impulse of a fluid directed toward an "attracting" body. From the data he collected he concluded that gravitation ought to propagate at the rate of at least 100 million times the speed of light, considering its velocity to be infinite.

Michael Faraday also conceived of space as a field with lines of force flowing like a river in which planets and stars floated along. The concept of an ether field or fluid was dropped with the coming of Einstein, because his famous equation required no medium in space for the transmission of light.

THE GEOMETRY OF THE COSMOLOGICAL CONSTANT

Thus far I have discussed two gravitational forms. The first form of gravity is a steady state acceleration, an "outflinging" of energy, which clumps itself into primal matter. The second form of gravity is that very same primal energy, no longer accelerating, but now bending around what has been transformed into mass.

*English translation, 1825, Chapter 7, book 10, Section 22, pages 642-645.

The now-existent mass curves the space/time energy around it so that this ether energy becomes a pressure to the mass.

Last but not least, we can address the pure ether field itself as being not only the substance of all things, but being the essence of pure gravity itself, a universal holding force connecting creation to God Himself. This pre-time energy originates, as I said, from the central creation event, and through it all things are connected to Him as though by a cosmic umbilical cord.

All matter is bonded via this primal field with a push/pull force. Let me illustrate. Take a small weight and attach it to a length of string; now begin to swing the weight around overhead. What do you observe? Clearly, two forces are at work from one single source of energy connected to a central event—you. The first force is the energy outflowing along the string from the center whipping the weight outward. The second force flows back down the string you hold, which resists the outflinging weight. The weight wants to go "out" due to the first energy, but at the same time the string force tugs back on it, establishing a dynamic.

Observe now a third phenomenon: It is the essential orbital structure, the basic geometry of the whole universe as it is held together. The orbit of the outflinging weight of cosmic mass is caused by its attachment to the central outflinging force, both a push and a pull force. If I read Einstein's Cosmological Constant correctly, he is not as wrong as he thought he was. The string in my analogy is really the outflinging force out of which the universe was first clumped, held then in orbital obedience to the force connected to the creation event. Here we have the one original force becoming both a push and a pull phenomenon, creating the gravitational geometry of the cosmos.

The three-dimensional shape of the universe is defined by the motion of the circumorbital outflinging, balanced by a pulling gravity. The outflinging and the gravity are two forms of the same energy, made possible by the presence of mass. Without mass none of these forms would be defined, no outflinging, no tugging, and hence, no geometrical structure. This is also true of subatomic particles held together by nuclear forces. Perhaps you can see how our planetary system would cease to exist if our sun were to "let go" of its orbiting planets. The myriad variations of the "push/pull outflinging" hold together the essential structure of matter. If you let go of your string, the weight will fly straight out. Its two-dimensional orbital form and vital structure would be lost. Likewise, in the cosmos, were you to break the bond with the Creation Center, everything would be flung into chaos. If this occurred down to the subatomic level, all matter would cease to exist—everything would reduce to pure energy.

The three-dimensional spherical shape of the universe is the result of the circumorbiting form of the pre-time force. The push-pull connection of this outward-bound force is essential to the existence of the universe. The outward-bound ether energy, attached to all its creations from the center, exerts an intelligent, civilizing restraining order on all matter. It is absolutely essential that the universe and all it contains continually remain bathed in, and attached to, the center creation event, lest God let go of "the string." If this were to happen, the three-dimensional spherical form of the universe would cease to have structure, and matter would tend to fly straight out into oblivion. Of course, that's not quite what would happen. Time would immediately be unable to flow from all directions at once, and unable to sustain the three-dimensional succession and change factor of matter, which, becoming unraveled, would cease to exist.

Remember, while this energy sweeps the cosmos, sustaining the three-dimensional form, it goes on to become the fourth dimension of time, the self-same gravity pressure to the very matter clumped from its energy self.

As to whether the universe has a finite or infinite boundary, the answer is simple. It makes no difference—for the following reason.

An infinitely expanding universe would only require more Cosmological Constant energy to be played out from the creation event center. For a stable, finite border leading to the edge of the Void, the energy connection need only be maintained and sustained.

Isaac Newton had some daring ideas about an ether field, suspecting a connection between the ether field and gravity as well as gravity and the magnetic field. Twentieth Century science has said he was wrong, but I believe he was merely ahead of his time. Einstein was another man ahead of his time; he called his Cosmological Constant theory his "greatest blunder." He should never have doubted his magnificent intuition, for he may yet be proven right.

THE RIDDLE OF WEIGHT

Albert Einstein said that a person falling freely will not feel his own weight. A feather and a cannonball falling freely with respect to one another in a vacuum have the same "weight," which is to say that there really isn't any weight in that context. If we use this illustration of Einstein's accepted maxim, the entire concept of a "pulling gravity" collapses.

If bodies falling freely do not experience their own weight (presumably no matter how large their masses), whence then comes the weight associated with their internal pressures and with gravitational "pull?" Surely, the earth is falling around the sun as the moon is around the earth; so, either way, there ought to be precious little weight in either case. And yet we attribute a weight to these bodies as well as a pulling force to this weight.

Deep under the ocean surface the pressure is enormous. A submarine venturing down beyond its design capacity would eventually collapse, crushed by the tremendous pressure. Understanding where the force of weight upon its hull comes from, no one would logically conclude that the submarine "pulled itself in." Of course, we would see that the awesome pressure of the water had transferred its energy to the hull. So it is with space/time pressure that exerts a pushing force on everything it surrounds.

This explains why a smaller mass has a diminished pressure (gravity) upon it. On the moon, an astronaut "weighs" just one sixth of what he would weigh on earth with the earth's gravitational pressure upon him. On the more massive planets, a person would hardly be able to walk.

The implications of being able to see gravity as a push or a squeeze, as a transfer of energy from a rushing space/time medium, are enormous. Science has much to benefit from recognizing that space is not a void.

Isaac Newton said that any mass is attracted to every other mass with a force directly proportionate to the sum of both masses inversely as the square of the distance between them. The chair upon which you sit has its own minuscule gravity, vastly overshadowed by the forces of pressure directed against the earth. All mass warps time moving around it with a pressure proportionate to its size. The energy flowing toward the earth from the time curve carries the chair, pressing it (and you along with it) to the surface. Therefore any object caught in this push flow gives the appearance of falling, of being pulled towards the earth.

After an object hits the lowest point in its fall, the energy pushing it (the pushing lines of force) continues on through toward the earth's center with its lines of force converging at the center from every conceivable direction, causing such compression that heat is generated at the core.

A large mass is more or less energy neutral, which is to say that its energy is bound up in its atoms, and so, it has little or no free energy of its own to cause gravity. To consider gravity as a property of mass doesn't make sense. Happily, Sir Isaac Newton's law continues to apply because the "gravity of pulling" and the "gravity of pushing" are mathematically identical. Therefore, despite this reversal in perspective, any two material objects in the universe will still attract each other with a force proportionate to the mass of the objects, with a ratio that diminishes inversely with the square of their distance apart.

WEIGHT AS RESISTANCE TO MOTION

In the "vacuum" of space, a feather and a cannonball weigh the same in free fall. Even though their masses differ, they do "weigh" the same, according to Einstein, which is to say that they don't weigh anything. In space, an astronaut sitting on his ship transfers no pressure to it. Even if this multi-ton spacecraft were to be on "top" of him, he would not feel the weight of it. Why? Because both would be "falling" in uniform motion with respect to one another, just as the feather falls with respect to the cannonball. The best way to explain weight is as a resistance to motion, and in this new theory, gravity resists the motion pressure of the time stream coming from every direction at once.

There is absolutely no difference between weight and gravity; they are one and the same. Remember, it is the steady state acceleration—gravity equivalence—that originally pressed energy into mass. This mass, once appearing in space/time, no longer requires a steady state for its gravity but acquires an equivalent push pressure and that is the Equivalence Principle—the push pressure of the warping of space/time force converging on mass.

Thus, there are two kinds of gravity and both are pressures, not attractions. One is Einstein's steady state acceleration, and the other is space/time warped by mass. One requires steady state acceleration for the pressure of gravity while the other does not.

HOW NEWTON'S ATTRACTION LAW STILL APPLIES

As I have said, Newton's law of attraction, whereby the moon and the earth pull on each other, is mathematically unaffected by the principles of gravitational "push" as opposed to the accepted gravitational "pull." When it comes to observable phenomena, the two theories are no different.

However, the "push" theory creates another dynamic that may involve an attraction phenomenon. The two bodies, I believe, actually compete for the same ether force in the intervening space. In other words, the earth and the moon draw from the same space/time flow.

Ordinarily the velocity of an orbiting object keeps it from falling into the larger mass. This is understood. But with two massive objects like the earth and the moon, we may possibly be observing another dynamic at work, one that involves the competition for the space/time energy between the bodies. Thus, while the moon's velocity is sufficient to keep it orbiting around the earth, it may not be bonded in the way we think. There is this other factor involved that acts like a space suction, binding the two bodies together.

The moon would obviously fall to the earth were it not for the motion of its orbit. However, since the moon is a significant mass, having its own time distortion energy competing with that of the earth in the intervening space, it is my contention that there is a kind of suction between them creating a tension that further connects the two bodies.

This new way of looking at gravitation still has the effect of keeping the moon "falling around" the earth, with its centrifugal motion keeping it from being pushed toward the earth. There is indeed a gravitational pull, but it is a tug in the space between the bodies giving the impression of an attraction intrinsic to the bodies themselves.

THE PROBLEM OF THE TIDES

Science tells us that the moon affects the tides. This is true, but let me explain this phenomenon in a different way. If you can accept the possibility that space is not a void, then consider the inevitable effect a flowing force would have on two bodies that are close to each other. Logically, they each would interrupt the natural effects of the flowing force by simply blocking the *flow* to one degree or another. To put it another way: If the pre-time force were somehow to express itself as light, one would be able to observe a growing shadow as two objects approached each other, each object casting a shadow on the other by blocking this "luminous pre-time force."

If you can imagine pre-time force as a constantly flowing gravitational push, then it is not hard to see that when this pressure—exerted on all sides of a body in space—is then interrupted by another body, you would have a change in the *push-force* gravitational influences. Ironically, the expression "rising tide" is not only poetic but is also scientifically accurate. The ocean is not *pulled* by the moon's gravitational influence (as is commonly believed), but, instead, literally "rises" and "falls" as the weight of pre-time force is partially relieved and reasserted by the passing interference (the shadow) of the orbiting moon. In this way, the orbit of the moon affects the ocean tides by "dragging" the water around by the moon's orbital influence.

There are two key aspects to this gravitational phenomenon caused by bodies approaching each other in space. The first is the "shadow" effect on the surface, and the second is the "vacuum" effect in the space between the two bodies. Remember, the pre-time force exerts essentially equal pressures on all sides of mass in space. Therefore, it would follow that the pressure between approaching objects would be less and less (in proportion to the law of the inverse square of the distance apart), tending to cause a greater and greater "vacuum" of pre-time force between them, not only on the surface which causes the tides, as I have said, but also out into the space between the two bodies.

As two objects approach one another, the mutual vacuum/shadow areas would increase by virtue of the increasingly blocked pre-time force flow. The diminishing pressure in the space between the two objects, in effect, acts somewhat like a vacuum, causing a tendency to come together. Supporting that tendency are the prevailing pre-time lines of force on the space side of the objects which are pushing them together. The closer the objects come to each other, the greater the absence of force between them, and the greater the effect of the "outside" push. Two objects of equal size and density would be lighter with respect to the "vacuum" between them, causing the *effect* of attraction between them while actually being pushed together.

After all is said and done, the net result is a pulling, but not because gravity pulls, rather because it pushes. The shadow/vacuum does the "pulling" as the moon, by its orbital motion, tends to pull away from the earth.

Sixteen

HOW LIGHT DOES THE IMPOSSIBLE

*"For the rest of my life
I will reflect on what light is!"*

Albert Einstein, c. 1917

Einstein wasn't the first great scientist to struggle with the impossible behavior of light. Before him, Michael Faraday, James Clerk Maxwell and others tried to understand what light was and how it moved. In 1864, Maxwell's calculations led him to a startling conclusion "that light and magnetism are affections of the same substance, and that light is an electromagnetic disturbance propagating through the field according to electromagnetic laws."

The field to which Maxwell referred was the ether field. It seemed obvious to him and scientists of his era that wave motion was propagated, carried by some kind of medium. They felt this had to apply to light as well. Just as sound needs air to travel, light would require some kind of space medium—the ether field. In 1887 Maxwell wrote the following for *Encyclopedia Britannica*: "Whatever difficulties we may have in forming a consistent idea of the constitution of the ether, there can be no doubt that interplanetary and interstellar spaces are occupied by a material substance or body." He was close, very close. It is there, but it is not "material." It happens to be the essence from which this universe is formed. In other words, ether is not of this world.

Thirty years later, the material concept of ether was overturned and replaced by Einstein's "etherless" Theory of Relativity. Ironically, while the concept of a material ether was first rejected by Einstein, he later rethought the matter and suggested that perhaps light itself might constitute some kind of "rehabilitated ether." So even in a 20th Century which has all but ignored it, ether theory is not really dead but lives on in those who seek it in a more subtle "immaterial" guise. The ether in my theory (pre-time force) is presented as a dark light that pre-exists light as we know it. Although this mysterious "dark ether" has not yet been scientifically recognized, it does indeed exist. What if this ether, which we sense most directly as gravity, somehow pre-exists all material substance—including energy itself? What if it is both the creator of light and the medium through which light propagates?

I will endeavor to show that both the theoretical corpuscular event of light (the photon) and the wave aspect of all electromagnetic motion through space, absolutely require the infinite velocity of this mysterious ether to push them along like "leaves blown in the wind." Allow me to explain.

Since it is an accepted maxim of science that in a vacuum light leaps out instantly at a *constant* 186,000.272 miles per second from any emitting source, let's not resist the obvious question here—how does light do that? What is even more perplexing is that light does not need its emitting source for power. Light slows down through the denser media of air, water, or glass, but upon emerging from the other side of any one of those media, light instantly *accelerates back* to its precise former velocity. Again, we are bound to ask how such a thing is possible. Where does light get its power, and how does light know how fast to go?

We know so much about light, but we do not know this. Surely this kind of mystery is far more fascinating than the rest of all our knowledge about light, because it has to do with the core question—what energizes light? And why is this energy self-regulating and constant? To ignore this mystery, while researching other aspects of light's behavior, takes the fun out of science. So let's consider the mystery further.

If I throw a baseball through a plate glass window, will it emerge from the other side at the same velocity? Of course not. Then how on earth do photons do it? From what source do they derive the power to regain their velocity? The answer to this happens to be a vital clue to the riddle of existence, staring science in the face for over a century.

The problem presented by this heretofore unexplained behavior of light is possibly too scary for most scientists to contemplate. The reason is that beyond this riddle lies the spiritual/metaphysical cause of the whole of reality. It marks the border where the explainable becomes inexplicable, tending to kick their collective egos into a denial mode—possibly a meltdown. Precious few scientists are capable of following a line of inquiry that will lead directly to a "religious" conclusion—the existence of a Creator in another dimension, One who not only makes the "ether wind" blow, but brings light out of darkness and somethings out of "no things."

As I see it, there are just two possibilities that science might entertain to explain the acceleration and re-acceleration of light. The first one is that light is both pushed and regulated by an external force, an ether "wind" of some kind.

The other possibility is that light has some kind of infinite, self-regulating, internal propulsion. Obviously, the first is the only plausible line of inquiry. So this writing will follow the concept of an undetectable ether timewind blowing constantly with an infinite velocity, carrying light and related magnetic waves on the current of "time."

EXPLAINING THE MYSTERY

Drop a pebble into a smooth, still pond and watch the ripples made at the disturbance center move out in concentric waves.

Electromagnetic waves behave somewhat like this, except that they are also pushed by that mysterious timewind. Strike a match and observe light leap instantly, radiating out in all directions at once at light velocity from its emitting point of excitation. If light is composed of particles (science is uncertain), these particles would move in a fashion similar to the waves on that smooth pond, but also blown by those mysterious currents of timewind that affect electromagnetic waves.

While ripples in a pond are driven entirely by the energy of origin inherent in the disturbance, both light and electromagnetic waves are carried by something more—as if the pond itself were moving.

If that smooth pond surface were a smooth moving river, any ripples made in the direction of the flow would surely travel farther (and more quickly) along with the river.

Now visualize a universe with an infinite amount of smooth invisible rivers of force, flowing from every direction and converging at every point in space, including where you are now sitting. There are "flows" coming from behind you and also coming towards you, going beyond—they come from above and below, in fact, from every direction.

If you could see all these lines of force passing through you, they would seem to emanate from you as an unseen "radiance" when they emerge. However, these lines of force become evident when you light a match or send a radio signal, because that disturbance (like the ripple made in the smooth flowing medium) is carried away on that smooth river in all three dimensions at once. With light, these lines of force are made visible.

With radio electromagnetic waves, ripples in the smooth three-dimensional river background are carried at light velocity away from you, driven by a "wind" that moves billions of times the velocity of light itself. The reason weak radio signals carry so far is that they do not move by their own energy. Ripples from the signal source are carried in ever-widening three-dimensional cycles until those waves (ripples in the smooth moving background) are too diluted to be detected.

I emphasize that neither light nor electromagnetic waves move under their own power! Disturbances occur at any emitting point where those "wind" currents converge; lines of force then carry light waves out and away in all directions at once, making a detectable radiance, especially with respect to light.

WHAT LIMITS LIGHT/WAVE VELOCITY?

At this point I have explained what blows or moves light along, but I haven't fully explained in this chapter what limits its velocity. Earlier I said that the force of the "wind" in one direction pushes light so quickly (instantly) that it would easily reach a limitless velocity (that of the ether wind) were it not governed by the same ether force coming from the opposite direction.

Earlier in this book, I explained that these lines of force are like phantom trains approaching one another on the same track and passing through one another. You see, these ether winds are not matter; they do not obey any physical laws. They happen to be the reason why there are physical laws to begin with. They are pre-matter, pre-light—in fact, pre-everything. Thus, as a photon is picked up at the point of excitation and blown down one of those tracks, the velocity of it is limited by the regulating wind coming down the track in the opposite direction.

The following question might occur to the reader: If a particle of light is carried along by the ether wind, and regulated by its exact opposing ether wind, why would that light not be affected by the trillions of other directional ether winds that are blowing on it at every moment?

The answer is that as light travels by way of its natural emitting pressure, only its exact directional partners have continuous contact with it, both pushing and limiting. Because of the tremendous speed of a light particle, it does not present itself long enough to be moved by any crossing line of force. Only its exact directional partners can both move and regulate its constant.

In this way, the true direction of each emitted particle of light acts like a track that is affected only by the lines of force that "ride" that track exactly. Light's original emitting force characterizes its motion because once its direction is defined by the focus of the emitting movement, the line of force moving in that direction carries the light particle forward until the opposing force creates a pressure barrier, limiting the speed precisely, and thus defining light velocity.

I should add that the crosswinds coming from infinite angles and directions do affect a light particle in this way; by constantly buffeting the particle from every direction, they contribute to its three-dimensional spin, a motion all matter must have in order to be sustained as matter.

Anywhere a light beam is focused it will radiate in that direction, propelled by a faster-than-light wind, slowed by the resisting "wind" to precise light velocity. No matter which direction light is beamed, there will always be an opposing and regulating resistance.

True mass does not escape being influenced by this phenomenon. Any attempt to push gross mass towards light velocity will be met with a steady state acceleration resistance (weight) which Einstein said is indistinguishable from gravity. The difference between the reaction of light and mass to this "space wind" is, as I said, that light is "feather-like" in that it is literally blown in one direction and regulated in the other. Matter, on the other hand, would be resisted only as it approached light velocity. Matter requires its own acceleration since it is too "heavy" to be blown by any "wind."

Just as light velocity is limited by the wind, so also is mass. The precise velocity limit of mass is not yet known. In any case, there is not sufficient available power to accelerate mass anywhere near light velocity. The energy required for a steady state acceleration (creating the equivalent to gravity) would make mass heavier and heavier as it went faster and faster. The faster it is pushed, the heavier it would become, requiring ever more pushing power. In order to travel at the speed of light, matter would literally need to dematerialize into light.

Were it possible for you to travel at light speed on a photon, the pre-time wind from behind your direction of motion would still pass you by, going millions or perhaps billions of times faster than you, beyond into infinity. No matter how much you travel towards infinity, it remains the same infinite distance away. Thus one can never know from just this evidence whether the universe is expanding outward or spinning round and round with the force continuously overtaking and passing you by in its cycles.

The constancy of light velocity also tells us that these smooth lines of force overtaking you (and resisting) are just as constant in their immeasurable velocity. If the regulator were irregular, it could not regulate light to a constant velocity.

The main reason a man can take a small, low-power transceiver, perhaps a hand-held two-way radio, and broadcast a message over huge distances is that the electromagnetic radio waves are carried in every direction by the smooth background motion of the "luminiferous" ether wind. The smooth motion carries the "dent" or wave disturbance made in it, requiring a sensitive enough receiving device to retrieve the pattern of wave resonance. The point I want to make is this: What if it were possible to go beyond just retrieving radio waves that are carried by the ether energy, and instead, tap into the ether energy itself? What kind of receiver or device would it take? If this energy does indeed exist, then it must be ubiquitous, which is to say, existing everywhere in the universe. If the pre-time wind moves faster than matter and light, then there must be an energy differential.

A wind generator must have a wind to create the necessary differential. The wind must blow for there to be energy available for conversion to electricity. My contention is that this ether energy is "blowing" everywhere constantly, and if we can recognize its existence, we might be able to tap into a clean, endless source of energy, not only for a better life here on earth, but for our journey to the stars.

Summing up: I began a previous chapter by saying that a large mass in space, like the earth, warps and captures these ether-wind energy lines of force, causing a downward pressure we know as gravity. Then ether lines of force also converge at the center of the planet, creating heat as well as lining up the atoms, thus causing the planet to rotate. This spinning magnetic field goes on to create an electric field that we commonly observe in lightning storms. Therefore the earth itself is an exemplar of everything I've said concerning this space wind, for the earth is a perpetual-motion generator, transforming the ether wind into gravity, heat, magnetic fields, and electric fields. This energy is all around us. We should recognize its origins. It's about time.

Seventeen

THE DIVINE ORIGIN OF LIGHT

*"Light is not as much
something that reveals,
as it is, itself, a revelation."*

Artist James De Nevel

What I am about to say I have said before with regard to ether and gravity. Now consider the ether theory with respect to light. What is light? We know this much: It is a form of energy with many remarkable characteristics and apparent contradictions. The nature of light baffles and defies the probing of experts. A scientific feud has been raging for well over 100 years, all the more amazing considering the spectacular advances in technology and knowledge. Ironically, it seems that the more we know, the less we understand. The closer scientists look at the behavior of light, the more confused they become. Why would this be so?

Their collective reasoning for wanting to understand the behavior of light is surely a practical one; mine, on the other hand, is more philosophical. What can the behavior of light tell us about the making of the universe? In order to make my case, allow me to state the historical dilemma confronting scientists with regard to light. Light, they observed, sometimes behaves like a wave, and at other times like a particle, a contradiction that science is hard pressed to explain.

Let us begin our investigation with what is already known: Mass is energy, and energy is mass, just as Einstein said. Bear with me please, as I endeavor to show that if you magnify the smallest particle to its greatest possible magnification, you will actually see that energy (wave) and mass (particle) are almost indistinguishable.

Today's theoretical physicists would have a better chance to determine the nature of light had not 20th Century science, led by Albert Einstein, determined that space was void of lines of force. Einstein rejected the widely accepted but unproven notion that space contained a flowing "something" called "luminiferous ether," a medium through which it was thought light propagated in the same way that sound uses air to travel.

As I have said, by rejecting the space ether theory, science took a wrong turn in the road, leading to the dead-end dilemma we now face. A kind of "ether" does indeed exist, but not quite like those ether theories of the 19th Century—it involves something less tangible. The reason why this ether is difficult to detect is that it has no easily measurable mechanical properties. It almost doesn't exist in this dimension of ours.

We are dealing here with a quintessential essence, which I have called pre-time force. This force field existed before creation, and still precedes everything in terms of physics; it is a field that I say is the elusive unified field that gave birth to creation, and continues to do so while sustaining and "mothering" it. This field is felt by creation as time, that which Einstein says is warped by the presence of mass. This "warping" of the field, of what becomes time to mass, converts those imponderable lines of force into measurable lines of force which we call gravity—a push force and not a pull force as is currently theorized.

Physicists have the same problem with light that they do with gravity, in that they have failed to see gravity as a variation of the expression of the ether field which they claim does not exist. They have arrived, therefore, at the mistaken notion that gravity is a property of matter rather than an effect of the field, which I say light is also. Although physicists understand a great deal about the uses of light and gravity, the causes of these phenomena lie beyond their comprehension. This is due to their incorrect belief that space is an etherless void, when in fact, as I have said before, matter could not possibly exist, let alone move, in the barren stillness of a true etherless void.

The universe is alive with this regulating ether force; it is an organic system. It is not a dead thing, as many believe, full of objects and energies cast adrift by some unfathomable explosion, later to ignite into life randomly. Rather, the universe lives and breathes order, and this "space ether" is the blood of its veins, with "God Force" as its continual pumping heart. Again, think of the lines of force that create this ether as currents of a river; you will then begin to understand how light is carried along in this stream at 186,000.272 miles per second.

Earlier in this work I mentioned Descartes' concept of the cosmos as swirling streams of water in which planets and stars float, moved along in the current like twigs and leaves. Faraday conjectured that such streams might be lines of force, a sea of pure forces. Actually, Faraday's theory was much closer to reality than other ether theories. His "lines of force" were not a ponderable substance in that they lacked measurable mechanical properties. Faraday said that such forces form themselves into myriad different forms and patterns creating chemical species, evolving a "fully corporeal world" as he put it. I agree.

For Faraday, the root of everything was this imponderable substance. These lines of force (which I claim to be pre-existent) emerge like the fury of a hurricane from the absolute center of rest, also undetectable and pre-natural.

I repeat, the reason such lines of force are close to impossible to detect is that they are made of the "no-thing" of "pre-existence" and are thus nonexistent to the senses. They are apparent only to the theoretician's "mind's eye," a disadvantage to a faithless empirical scientist who needs to be able to see, touch, or probe in order to believe. If you will consider the universe in the context of this theory of all theories, then I can show you a totally logical path that leads right to the heart of cosmic causality.

LIGHT • WAVICLES • WHIRLPOOLS

Perhaps you have observed those tiny whirling pools in a river. What they call a photon behaves something like that. River eddies are actually made up of the river's current, differing from the current only in the shape of their flow. They are whirlpools, spinning and converging on their centers. Just as a river eddy is made up of swirling current, likewise the photon is the swirling energy of the "luminiferous ether" (the current of the pre-time force).

My concept of this "ether" is that it is composed of those lines of pre-time force I have discussed. Even if one cannot prove the existence of the ether "wind" or current, its manifestation (the photon/eddy) bears witness to it as a visible effect spun from an invisible cause. As you will see presently, photons of light (just like river eddies) have their own ways of expressing the current that also sustains them—some are larger and some are smaller.

Remember, in the beginning of this work I described the smallest particle as an origitron, a specific creation of the wind current—an energy whirlpool clotting or clumping out of the ether wind. On the other hand, the photon may not be quite like that; most likely it is a much larger particle, not so much directly created by the "wind," but carried along and sustained by it. However, in a broader sense, it still results from the swirl of the current.

The existence of the invisible ether wind or current in space/time is represented also as the visible eddy-like phenomenon of the photon, the knowable effect of an unknowable cause. No river eddy can exist alone; if there's no current, there's no eddy. In the same way, were there no ether current, there could be no origitrons and thus no photons or any other larger forms of matter. Each current (whether river current or space ether) causes the swirl, sustains the swirl, and pushes it along. These swirls are the basic building blocks of what we know as matter.

So "that which appears is made by that which is not seen," as the Bible says. All matter—including light—is made manifest by the same invisible power. *Sub*-subatomic particles exist closer to the border of what is creation and what is before creation; they exist on the edge of time and pre-time, that flowing energy field which cannot be seen, probed, or proven simply because it is made of the "stuff" of pre-existence. What exists for us is its matter manifestation. What exists for us is the swirl but not the river. Our eyes cannot behold the space-ether river; we see only the swirl. Cosmically, the swirl is creation itself while the river is the essential force field behind creation, continually becoming creation.

THE SUBSTANCE OF THINGS UNSEEN

It is interesting how we discover things inadvertently. One day I was sitting by my pool, watching water flowing in from the filter pump. What I noticed was that the swirls of water pushed along in the current caused shadows on the bottom of the pool, just the way a solid object does. The inflowing current itself didn't cast a shadow, and yet its swirling eddies did— some of them spinning so tightly as to cast very dark shadows.

The swirl is the water and the water is the swirl. There shouldn't be any difference, and yet there was; the swirling motion of the water coming out from the pump acted like a solid object by casting a shadow.

From a distance, and for analogy's sake, one can view that swirl as a "particle," not only because it casts a shadow but because the spinning motion causes this pseudo-particle to resist the motion of the current, it being, in a sense, "heavier" than the stream. By virtue of its spinning "mass," the water swirl hangs back in the current much the same way that a photon "particle" does in space/time. Mass is defined by its resistance to motion.

When energy spins, the gyroscopic effect of its own motion gives it "weight," which we call mass. This weight has a predictable effect: The "weight" of the energy swirl resists being pushed. Thus the swirls in the current of cosmic energy cause themselves to go slower than the "ether" stream in which they are spinning; like the eddy in my pool, these "particles" (or "wavicles") are detectable whereas the "ether" stream is not. The beauty of this model is that it makes more understandable how there can be a transition phenomenon of the invisible into the visible, the undetectable into the detectable, and solves the problem of what light is.

THE PSEUDO-SOLID

Light "wavicles" are pseudo-solids. If the reader has trouble considering a whirlpool as a solid, these wavicles may also be compared to chunks of ice pushed along in a strong current. Like the whirlpool, here again the water is the ice and the ice is also water. The ice is one of the manifestations of water, and yet when the ice is pushed along by the current, a wave appears from behind due to the pushing of the current. This pushing provides another set of waves surrounding our pseudo-solid wavicle, the photon/eddy. Like chunks of ice, non-solid river eddies also have extra waves around them as they are pushed along. Photon/eddies are like that; these shivers in space caused by the motion of light through the ether may well be the electromagnetic (radio) waves detected in light's spectrum.

Using our river eddy example, we can now better understand the wavicle behavior of the photon. Not only does it spin inwardly, driven by the current, but its spinning mass-like effect creates "weight;" that is to say, it produces additional waves around it as it resists the push force of the ether current.

The wave effect caused by the wavicle will vary depending on its "mass." Remember, we are talking about two kinds of wave phenomena. One is the swirl of the wavicle itself and the other is the wave caused by the mass-like swirl, acting much like the bow of a ship plowing through the ocean.

Scientists have observed an inexplicable phenomenon. Using modern technology they can observe light and see it as a wave, and yet a moment later observe it as a particle. Some quantum physicists have reached the point where they believe this change might be somehow *actually caused* by the observer himself.

I have a different theory. If one looks closely enough at the light phenomenon, there will be a point at which the definition of wave and particle becomes blurred, where the edge of the particle at its perimeter fuses into the "ether" wind and becomes a "bow wave" sending out shivers diminishing in space. Remember, the wavicle acts as a wave sometimes and at other times like a particle, and it really can be one or the other depending on how closely it is observed. It is a whirlpool mass with additional waves around it. Close up, it looks like a wave (swirl), but from further back it appears as a particle.

THE MORE-UNCERTAINTY PRINCIPLE

The Uncertainty Principle of Quantum Physics has specific application, but here I take a different approach to "uncertainty." This principle is simply a variation of the relativity theme. Let me explain. We look up at the moon while at the same time astronauts on the moon look up at us. So, which way is up? What is "up"? Is there no "down"?

Clearly, what is "up" is relative to the observer's frame of reference. By the same token, "how far" or "how close" also alters the relativity and, hence, alters the appearance of an object, as well as the effect the object can have on the observer's environment.

A case in point: A human face magnified becomes a pock-marked "lunar surface." Closer examination causes the scene to change many times. We observe bacteria and viruses, monster antibodies gobbling up germs swimming in a Sargasso-like sea. Beyond that comes the inner space, the micro-cosmos of whirling electron moons. If we go far enough, we find those tiny origitron wavicles on the border of time and timelessness, creation and pre-creation. And all this on the face of a pretty girl.

So then what is in a face? Is a face a face, an eye an eye? Is a blade of grass a blade of grass? How is anything defined? Of what can we be certain? Obviously, the answer lies in how close-ly you care to look. Our physical reality is defined relatively—how far away or how close are we? That, in essence, is what makes science so uncertain. Human beings, as creatures of pure cause-and-effect relativity like other things of nature, are affect-ed by their immediate environment. An ant sees and experiences only what is relative to an ant. Human beings do not experience as ants do but have instead relative experiences of their own. However, we have the unique opportunity to see, even "travel," beyond our relative existence to all the others, and ultimately (spiritually) to the core truths. Without God as a reference, this gift of consciousness is confounded. In life, as in science, our missing relative, God, provides His objective view, making everything understandable and beautiful.

Because most quantum physicists function without including the Missing Relative in their calculations, they operate in a confounded state in which they can be convinced that the observer *actually changes* the outcome of that which is observed. The truth is that the nature of physics is not really changed by mere human observation. Reality is only redefined; where or what we are simply gives us a different perspective toward the same reality. Our presence cannot change reality; only God can do that.

The ego-intellectual journey toward knowledge is away from understanding. It is tantamount to partaking of the forbidden fruit. Nothing can be truly understood from the flotsam and jetsam of disconnected intellectual knowledge, because the more we know the more we stand before the next thing we don't know; it is all relative. For every answered question, a thousand more appear. Even the knowledge we do collect is dry, like the dead grains of sand on a beach. And after we have proudly collected the whole beach, what do we have? Nothing, really, just a false sense of achievement—dispiriting and ultimately useless to the soul. Those who seek only intellectual knowledge take a journey away from consciousness, away from the light of understanding; these people feed an ego appetite that can never be satisfied, producing only a "weariness of the flesh." Inevitably, after all their scientific searching, they are left holding nothing, staring into the cosmic darkness.

What science observes and thinks it knows is constantly changing. The more science knows and observes, the more insecure it becomes—a true irony. However, when we see the whole picture from the point of view of the creation event and the pre-time force, which is the unified field, then we can reconnect to our moorings.

Wherever you are, magnify any object, a face, a leaf, a piece of wood, whatever; go deep inside, and you will eventually arrive at this border. You will confront that same unified cosmos, the "beyond," that single reality that connects everything to Him. Here, just as in outer space, origitron wavicles whirl and spin, dividing existence from the "non-existence" of the pre-time force.

In a wordless way He whispers in our soul, "Behold I make the tree; I make the flower and the bee; I am the air you breathe; I am the food that nourishes, I am the all, the everything but no thing. Harken, prideful one, the more you try to know, the more I will make you realize how little you understand. Now believe that without Me nothing is meaningful or certain. Be still and know that I am God."

When theologian Thomas Aquinas was on his deathbed, his assistant pleaded with him to finish his last book. Aquinas said, "I cannot." Urged once again, Aquinas said, "All that I have written is like chaff to me." And then he explained the mystical value of knowledge in his search for God:

That which is not known cannot be loved. Knowledge, therefore, is not to be loved for itself but is meant to lead to that which must be loved. When He whom is to be loved is found by virtue of knowledge, knowledge ceases.

Conclusion

*"I maintain that the cosmic religious
feeling is the strongest and noblest
motive for scientific research."*

Albert Einstein, 1930

I believe that the ancient Jewish and Christian mystics had knowledge about the origin of the universe beyond that of modern science. They knew by a faith that needed no scientific proof.

They knew the universe had a beginning and hence a Beginner; they knew that from no thing came every thing; they fathomed the unfathomable, and spoke of it in the limited language (and scientific understanding) of their time.

As a spiritual finishing touch to this work, allow me to copy the characteristic style and message of these mystics, believing that their flowing and poetic prose addresses itself more deeply, and therefore more accurately, to the mystery of the science.

The essentials of this work are now restated in this poetic form to the end that the reader will more fully grasp and appreciate the Spirit behind the creation of all the works of God the Father, Supreme Scientist and Savior of the world.

****

BEFORE THE BEGINNING, the Creator is. And in Him the universe pre-exists. All that is came from Him, and without Him not a single thing came into being out of that which was.

And so God enacted Will. And by Divine command, His Word alone, created He the heavens and the earth.

And so, out of the calm center of Universal Being flowed Divine Energy. Out of the Stillness it came, the primal motion of creation. Around and around it goes and comes, forming the spherical boundaries of the cosmos. And tiny things birthed from this force fall out, floating in the primal sea that is also time.

All that is, is in motion from the Stillness—compressed, spinning, moving in orbits, cycles and circles, around the Timeless Soul of Self.

Because the Timeless One enacted Will, there was energy; because of energy, motion; because of motion, matter; because of matter, space/time.

Divine Energy is all there is, manifesting in the all of creation as the seen and the unseen, The One revealed through the other.

From the Eternal Beyond comes now the infinite universe, a procession of energies, which, after being transformed into matter, become sculptured into all the glories of creation, infinitely unfolding, beauteous exemplars of all things pre-existing with God.

While sustaining the universe, the Divine Force also manifests as man's divine essence, the quickener of men's longing souls.

While God is incomprehensible, His essence can be seen in everything He creates. So how can those with perverse intellects, never having discovered how to separate their souls from the molecular bondage to their mortal natures, ever fathom what lies beyond nature's boundaries?

They can do little but dabble in equations, ascribing "understanding" to what is only the dryness of rote learning. Never will they experience the joy of realizing that God is in the universe and the universe is in God—One sustaining, the other being sustained.

While all things are sustained from the beginning by His reinforcing power, only man can reach inward toward the beginning to receive His direct Personal Essence, the like of which is reserved for the good angels and the children of the Light.

The malevolent ones are deprived of this intimate quickening. Whereas the inspired, being infilled with emanations of His primal essence, reflect His likeness in much the same way the moon acts as a secondary likeness to the sun. As the moon reflects the light of the sun, so too we achieve knowledge of the Son, and beyond Him, the Father. Whosoever partakes of this inner Universal Light also possesses spiritual power—a knowledge understood as faith to the degree to which he or she has matured in the Light.

True love for God is need. To need is to love. Not to need Him is a denial of Him and thus, to be filled up with the love of the world. Even love's true yearning comes from Him and goes back up to Him as the cry for redemption.

Thus does the absence of sensual passion and emotion in the pursuit of virtue constitute love for God, whereby Love has space to enter and displace the indwelling worldly evil, bringing with it, as God's love always does, all the bounty and blessings of the spirit. Those souls sweetened by means of God's infilling love reveal His Character within them.

Not even does the cosmos revolve about its own nature, except by the Spirit of its origin. All celestial motion turns about the Soul of itself, advancing, unfolding in succession and change through timeless times from the pre-existent Will.

For at the heart of the heavens there lies a timeless realm with no other place beyond. Such heavenly worlds, by virtue of their timeless nature, are ethereal. For what can be above nature except that which is spiritual? Where can there be anything so subtly formed?

That region beyond the spherical dimension of time cannot admit corporeal bodies such as ours. While flesh and blood cannot enter there, this does not prevent a soul from crossing the Stillness into this paradigm, purified of sensual attachments. This realm, while coexisting with ours, encompasses the boundary of the physical universe, since it is from this region the cosmos came.

And so it came to pass in assigning the boundaries between the paradigms of heaven and the material realms, the Majestic Craftsman set into motion the order of existence, and set within its finished order the triumph of all His creations, man reflecting His likeness—part heaven, part earth, a living soul in material form.

How delicately is man balanced in his respondings, and in their unfolding order. Observe the gravities, the material pulls upon his allegiance, how they pit him against the Spirit who made him spirit, in this very material world God also created.

And to what end, you may ask, is this conflict shaped? The direct answer would be to rob the mystery of its discovery, of the vital searching, beyond which there is life eternal.

Therefore, man, the created, is made different by virtue of this divine command whereby love born from freely chosen allegiance might one day bring forth abundant fruits now hidden and stored within man. And in the day of the perfect time, there will pour out true love, one for another and from each to all.

The Kingdom of Heaven is poised to receive the longing of the weary souls of the prodigal sons and daughters of the Father, who, after expending their essence on egocentric and selfish pursuits, having debased themselves by their own defiant wills, and being now spiritually impoverished, look forward with wistful longing to the realm of the kind Father, from Whom they were born separated—such repentant longing being the only love one can have for the Father.

All creatures, animal and man, possess life force, but the noetic nature of man possesses not only animal life but also the direct essence from God Himself, a unique attribute capable of quickening and transforming the soul of the being united with Him.

Angels, being inferior to man, do not possess this duality. They did not receive the earthly form and thus cannot animate the being they do not possess, and therefore cannot be redeemed, as man can be, from the body that contains his fall.

Therefore is the soul in the body a bridge between two worlds, whereby one acts through the other, and through which conduit His Will might manifest on earth. For unlike angels, it is from a body that the lost soul is redeemed.

And so each one in his stubborn pride misses not only the quickening of God's eternal life essence, but forfeits by way of denial the abundance of things to come.

For in the season of its selfishness, each soul has a self-existent essence similar to the Self-Existent One, a life essence potentially different from the temporal life of creatures, under the order of nature from the very beginning when God commanded, "Let there be."

And so while the first man had two origins, the noetic nature he fell from and the animal he fell to, mankind is now born first of nature to be reborn back into spirit. Oh fallen Adamic man! Behold the mercy of your God; your choice is yet unspent, and salvation is close at hand.

The first descending order ends now, full circle, complete to the Beginning. The quickening Spirit from the timeless realm from which the universe came and was pre-formed, enters now from within our longing for salvation as a rebirth, for the home of God is the softened, repentant heart of man.

Do not therefore inquire as to what your end shall be, for the yearning soul journeys back home, briskly returning like the prodigal son. For where the end of this journey is, here and now is the dawn of a new beginning. Seek (yearn) and find, knock and the door will open. He Awaits. Who has ears to hear, let him also understand.

AFTERWARD

*"Man must understand his universe
in order to understand his destiny..."*

Neil A. Armstrong, Astronaut

HOPES AND FEARS

In writing this book, my desire has been to inspire faith. Faith is what restores souls to God, and, of course, worship is the pathway to faith. What is worship, if not inspired wonder, and what could inspire wonder more than the magnificence of His Creation?

Just as art glorifies the artist, satisfying the needs of both the painter and the beholder, so is our awe, honoring the wonders of His creation, tantamount to worship of God. And He rewards our appreciation of His truths with the warmth of His in-filling love. Clearly, He is not confined to the stagnant dimensions of houses of worship made by human hands.

Alas, I write about the physics of the infinite with some trepidation. I remember seeing happy, carefree images of Albert Einstein as the young theorist full of optimism. How different were those pictures compared to the news footage of him taken later—after the atom bomb. How changed he was in the 1950s, his darker, careworn countenance etched with the worries of a nuclear world. No matter how well intentioned an idea, people can abuse it, as many a young physicist working now will learn. A philosopher or scientist never knows what will be done with his work. How could Einstein know that $E=mc^2$ would lead to a world bristling with nuclear weapons? Nevertheless, his Theory of Relativity, which predicted the enormous amount of energy stored in minute amounts of matter, made it all possible. No wonder Einstein's countenance seemed so very sad before he died.

I have presented in this book the possibility of a new kind of energy. Time, light/matter, and space are indeed relatives, as Einstein said, but there is a key missing relative—that of force. Time, space, and matter require an energizing and regulating universal force, a life-force if you will, which I call "pre-time force." It is true that the existence of this pre-time force, the original motion that emanated from the Original Stillness, could open up some fearsome scientific possibilities; however, there is a bright side. This theory could foster a greater appreciation of God and His purpose for us, increasing our collective faith in Him. For how could mankind deny the existence of God if it became scientifically evident that the whole universe unfolds from a single principle, and that space is infused with perpetual force? The answer to that question reveals the dark side of spirituality—man can deny God no matter what the evidence. Rebellion doesn't need reasons, although reasons are a useful hiding place.

Ironically, it is science that may reveal to the world the spiritual dynamic in life because, as the creation points to the Creator, those who hate God for no reason will show themselves more plainly. Many Biblical stories make it clear that man is capable of direct, knowing rebellion against God. Thus a theory like the one presented in this book, if proven to be true, will create a spiritual danger.

The discovery of a unified field would irresistibly point to an orderly universe, causing science to become a powerful force for truth. Once science starts to demonstrate the presence and the love of God through a greater understanding of His laws, there will be many in this world who will angrily rebel. In their deep hatred of God, they will descend to extremes of denial that could become terrifyingly dangerous, perhaps to the point of their venting an irrational fury against believers. Ironically, too, the discovery of a perpetual energy source may only goad the determined rebels into greater rebellion as they, in their outrageous pride, will seek to create a world that doesn't need God. Rebels have always used the gifts of God to spit in His face. And yet, for believers, and those who are willing to believe, this science will bring the purest joy.

With or without scientific revelations, this joy is available to all of us right now. Yes, we are born spiritual creatures, albeit subject to the space/time/matter continuum. But even so, we can discover and experience God—not merely to know Him intellectually through the pages of a science book or the Bible, but to earnestly and joyfully recognize and appreciate Him as our Ultimate Father, our Ultimate Relative, Creator Spirit, from Whom all things spring into existence.

What if that "still small voice," persistently following us as conscience, is really God Himself, always there, following us through our lifetime trying to save us? What if, in the ecstasy of a deep revelation, we were suddenly pulled free from our submersion in the gravity of time, the worldly succession of change and decay, the endless cycles of life and death? Would not our souls then be moved beyond the reach of time, saved by our connection to His Eternal Presence within us—what Saint Paul identified as "the Mind of Christ"?

Alas, being separated from Him in our current state of failing and disbelief, mankind remains bonded to the laws of creation. What is that flaw in our human nature that condemns us to the doom and gloom of dissolution in the corporeal universe, where everything that is born lives in a succession of change, decay, and death? That willful flaw is our pride, our ego, which *keeps* us earthbound and so submerged that we cannot see, let alone seek, His salvation, His right way.

I began this book by saying that there was something about death that troubled me as a child, that it seemed somehow out of order. Of course, death is part of God's plan, but it is not His plan that we submit to it in defeat. We are meant to have victory over death. What if we made our ultimate goal a search for this victory, this Ultimate Reality? What if we genuinely yearned to discover the mystery of our direct relationship with our Father God, who is the Supreme Relative, mankind's physical and metaphysical parent spirit?

What if the pain and angst we all feel is due to a separation caused by the "gravitational pull" of our animal egocentricity, drawing us away from the Father toward a black hole of self-centered, spiritual oblivion? Hell is a most terrible reality, but, thank God, it is not the only reality. What if our destiny, truly fulfilled, is to be saved from that ego pull, that death-centered, mortal world of time and space and matter—saved by Him who watches over us, the patiently waiting Heavenly Father who has loved us from the very beginning? He remains eternally beyond the time, space, and matter of His Creation—untouched by death—in the Heavenly realm where we ourselves ultimately belong. May it be so with you.

GLOSSARY OF TERMS

The argument of this book will be easier to follow if the reader has in mind (or at need refers to) the meanings of these terms:

• **CIRCUMORBIT:** (Verb) To orbit, or whirl about a center, in all directions simultaneously.

• **DISTORTED TIME:** The time through which objects travel, always faster than HONEST TIME.

• **ETHER FORCE:** A "wind" blowing constantly throughout the universe at a super velocity, carrying light, creating gravity, and regulating magnetic waves on the current of time. It is the same as PRE-TIME FORCE or Pre-physical Force, and is sensed in this dimension as time itself.

• **FIRST CAUSE STILLNESS:** That center of absolute rest, the field from which matter drops and expands centrifugally.

• **HONEST TIME:** The "time" that exists only at PRIMAL STILLNESS. It is not possible for matter to move slower than PRIMAL STILLNESS, which is the motion borderline of all mass, and is everywhere present in the universe.

• **KINETIC MOTION:** Kinesis is motion, so the phrase may seem redundant. It means motion-force, or a force that causes motion.

• **MOVING STILLNESS:** Motion without benefit of time. The divine paradox of motion and rest.

• **NOUMENON:** The abstract essence, not perceptible by the sense, that is the basis or cause of a phenomenon.

• **ORIGITRON:** The first subatomic matter, smallest of all light particles (perhaps *dark matter* itself), a whirling form caused by the pre-time motion under its own pressure. ORIGITRONS evolve into more complex arrangements—electrons, atoms, molecules.

• **PRE-TIME FORCE:** The continuing, limitless other-dimensional noumenon that energizes the universe, and emanates out of the still creation center that defines all motion.

• **PRIMAL STILLNESS:** The place at which space/time coordinates move synchronously with the FIRST CAUSE STILLNESS, first in the order of all relative "moving stillnesses." The slowest space/time in which matter can exist—the motion border line of mass, everywhere present in the universe.

• **STEADY STATE ACCELERATION:** Einstein's Equivalence theory which says that a steady state of acceleration creates an equivalence to gravity. This force is experienced commonly when riding a fast-accelerating elevator, feeling oneself pressed down on the floor. It is also experienced by astronauts at takeoff.

• **TIME STRINGS:** The invisible, perpetual tracks of the timewind that expand from a timeless center or creation event.

• **TIMEWIND:** The continuum by which time travels in all directions at once with a spirit-like quality that allows it to affect matter as well as move through itself. It is the circumorbiting PRE-TIME FORCE as sensed by matter, the force we perceive as gravity among other things.

• **WAVICLE:** This describes the peculiar behavior of light, which sometimes acts like a wave and sometimes like a particle.